Songs of the
Pacific Northwest

FOLK   TOPICAL   HISTORICAL

Kenai Community Library
163 Main Street Loop
Kenai, Alaska   99611

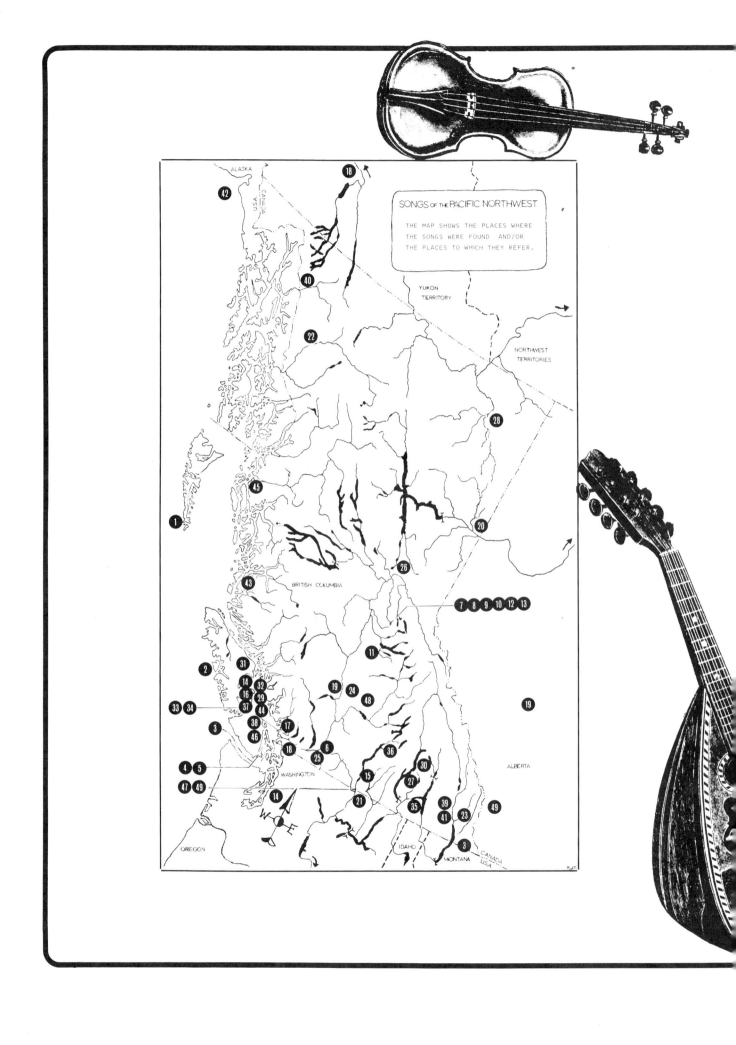

Songs of the Pacific Northwest

Philip J. Thomas

Music Transcription and Notation
By Shirley A. Cox

ISBN 0-88839-040-8 Soft
COPYRIGHT © 1979 PHILIP J. THOMAS

Cataloging in Publication Data

Thomas, Philip J., 1921-
    Songs of the Pacific Northwest

    Bibliography: p.
    Includes index.
    ISBN 0-919654-89-4 Hard
    ISBN 0-88839-040-8 Soft

    1. Folk-songs, Canadian-British Columbia.
2. Music, Popular (Songs, etc.)-British
Columbia. I. Title
M1678.T4S6   784.4'9'711   C78-002200-9

Design by Preston Denny

Cover art by Sheila A. Montgomery

Published simultaneously in Canada and the United States by:

hancock

house

HANCOCK HOUSE PUBLISHERS LTD.
3215 Island View Road   SAANICHTON, B.C. V0S 1M0

Contents

Foreword

This book of songs attempts to bring to life something of the story of British Columbia and its people. In the Pacific Northwest setting from the days of the early fur trade to the present, people have used their own songs to express and share their reactions to events. That the story told through them is so full and varied indicates a rich heritage in a land not generally recognized as having an English language song tradition.

Broadly speaking the songs can be called "folk songs." In addition to traditional songs and ballads, the term "folk song" may be given to newer and authored songs of the same general type if the writer's primary intent is social and communicative rather than commercial. Included are reworked or "parodied" songs and topical songs using traditional or popular tunes. Two-fifths of the songs presented here came to me in printed or written form, often preserved in public archives; the remainder were collected orally from singers in many parts of British Columbia. Of the hundreds of songs that I have collected in the province, this book includes most of the archival material, but only a selection of oral. A further book, now in preparation, will contain in addition to many of the traditional folk songs migrant in British Columbia, more of the songs created in the province, including a number of songs of social significance omitted from this volume for want of space.

In general the songs are arranged chronologically. Although presented under ten headings, the book falls into two main parts: first, the period from the early fur trade to Confederation in 1871; and second, from Confederation to the 1960's. In the second part songs are grouped around a number of themes — early transportation, pioneering settlement, and the several primary industries of British Columbia. Under various headings are a few songs touching on pioneer life in Alberta, the Yukon, Alaska, and Washington State.

With few exceptions the texts of the songs are the way they were collected. Some explanations of uncommon expressions have been placed in the margin beside the text or appear in the background notes accompanying the songs. In two instances after careful research, I have expanded fragments into songs which I hope reflect adequately the song's original intent as seen by my informants.

Acknowledgement of these changes can be found in the Appendix, which indicates sources.

The length of the background notes varies as I have felt the need to provide the historical context. The main references used in my research appear in the select bibliography.

The tunes for the songs come from two basic sources: the tape recorded singing of informants and printed music. Printed music of the 1860's was used, for example, for some of the Cariboo songs. For a few of the manuscript songs I have set older tunes or made new ones. I am grateful to Shirley A. Cox for the skill and sensitivity with which she has done the transcription of the songs. She has also provided chords for instrumental accompaniment. I have worked in consultation with the transcriber and take full responsibility for the final forms of the tunes. Sources of the tunes are included in the Appendix.

In collecting these songs I have depended on the goodwill and help of a great many people. My first debt is to the singers themselves. Their valuable contributions are now preserved in the Provincial Archives of British Columbia. Although from my earliest collecting in 1951, I discovered a few singers on my own, I was usually led to a singer by someone giving me the singer's name, and occasionally arranging for us to meet. Here I must mention especially Jeannie Moss, Vera Johnson, Barry Hall, Helen Embury, and Pat Graber, for they not only gave me singers but have in many ways been supportive over the years.

Others to whom I wish to express my gratitude for assistance in finding texts, printed music, illustrations (including photographs), and research materials for the background notes are Anne Yandle of Special Collections, U.B.C. Library; Willard E Ireland and his successor, Allan R. Turner, Provincial Archivist, and their staffs at the Provincial Archives of British Columbia, especially David B. Mason, Assistant Archivist, and Barbara MacLennan for her help with photographs; Ron D'Altroy of Historical photographs, Vancouver Public Library; and Stanley G. Trigg of the Photographic Archives, McCord Museum, Montreal. Other institutional facilities where staffs gave generous assistance were the Legislative Library, Parliament Buildings, Victoria, B.C.; the Northwest Collection, Vancouver Public Library; the Vancouver City Archives; the New York Public Library; Libraries at Brown, Harvard and Yale Universities and the University of Washington; the Peabody Museum, Salem, Mass.; Massachusetts Historical Society; the Oregon Historical Society; and the Public Archives of Canada, Ottawa.

Special thanks are due to Jon Bartlett, who checked and completed the verbal transcriptions, and whose general assistance in the preparation of the manuscript was invaluable. I must also express my appreciation to the Vancouver School Board and the Government of British Columbia for providing the time and financial support which enabled me to further my researches and complete this book.

Finally, I must thank Hilda L. Thomas whose critical reading of the manuscript as it progressed was indispensable.

Vancouver, B.C.   Philip J. Thomas

Pre-Colonial Times

Public Archives of Canada

Author photo

The Bold Northwestman.

COME all ye bold Northwestmen who plough the raging main,
Come listen to my story, while I relate the same;
'Twas of the Lady Washington, decoy'd as she lay,
At Queen Charlotte's Island in North America.

On the sixteenth day of June, boys, in the year Ninety-One,
The natives in great numbers, on board our ship did come,
Then for to buy their furs of them our captain did begin,
But mark what they attempted before long time had been.

Abaft upon our quarter deck two arm chests did stand,
And in them there was left the keys by the gunner's careless hand;
Thinking quickly, they procuring of them did make a prize,
Our captain he then speaking unto them did say,
Thinking we had no other arms for to defend our lives.
If you'll return me back those keys I forthe same will pay;

The captain then perceiving this would be our overthrow,
See that they are well loaded, be sure and don't miss fire,
He then spoke unto his people, likewise unto his officers prepare,
And to one said misfortune, few guns could we did repair,
We only found six pistols, a gun and two small swords.

He gave a signal I will give, it shall be a follow me,
Then down into the cabin straightway we did find there,
Our powder we got ready and gun room open lay,
Our souls we did commit to God prepar'd for a watery grave!
Till one of those blood-thirsty hounds he made a spring below.

All this time upon the quarter deck on poor man was forc'd to stand,
With twelve or fourteen of those savages with knives all in their hands;
Our captain then said "follow me," and felled him with a blow,
Then well, what few fire arms we had, we rush'd on deck again,

And by our being resolute, our quarter deck we gain'd,
Soon as we gain'd our arm chest such slaughter then made we,
And found we had nobody hurt, to work we went straightway,
That in less than ten minutes our deck they did enjoy.
Then we threw overboard the dead that on our deck there lay,

The number kill'd I upon our deck that day was sixty good,
We call'd all hands to quarters and the town did play away,
We made them to return what things they'd stolen that day.
And fall as many wounded as soon we understood,

'Twas early the next morning at the hour of break of day,
I'd have you all take warning and always ready be,
For to suppress these savages of Northwest America;
We sail'd along about the town which we came to straightway;

And when we shall old China we're fairly rolling on,
And now I shall conclude and make an end unto my song,
We'll drink good punch to which we've suffered long;
For they are no devious some proof to obtain America,
Where we shall drink a health and play,

Success unto the commander of the Lady Washington!
And fall in commemoration what on that day was done,
O may death and destruction always attend his foe.
And now I shall conclude and make an end unto my song,

Oregon Historical Society

The Bold Northwestman

Come all you bold North-west-men, who plough the rag-ing main, Come
lis-ten to my stor - y, while I re-late the same, 'Twas
on the Lad - y Wash-ing-ton, de-coyed as she lay At
Queen Char-lotte's Is - land, north - west of A-mer-i-kay.

1.

Come all you bold Northwestmen, who plough the raging main,
Come listen to my story, while I relate the same,
Twas on the *Lady Washington*, decoyed as she lay,
At Queen Charlotte's Island, Northwest of Amerikay.

2.

On the sixteenth day of June, boys, in the year of ninety-one,
The natives in great numbers on board our ship did come.
And for to buy the furs of them, our Captain did begin,
But mark what they attempted before long time had been.

3

Abaft upon our quarterdeck, two arm-chests did stand,
And in them there was left the keys, by the gunner's careless hand,
When quickly they procuring of them did make a prize,
Thinking we had no other arms for to defend our lives.

4.

Our Captain spoke unto them, and unto them did say,
"If you'll return to me those keys, I for the same will pay."
No sooner had he spoke those words, than they drew forth their knives,
Saying, "The vessel's ours, Sirs, and we will have your lives!"

Haida mortuary poles from Ninstints are an heraldic solemnization of individual achievements and status.

New England merchants had this medal struck in 1787 to mark the first American venture into the northwest coast sea-otter trade. Its heraldry plays a counterpoint to that of the leaders of Ninstints.

5.

Our Captain then perceiving the ship was in their power,
He spoke unto his people, likewise his officers,
"Go down unto the cabin, and there some arms prepare;
See that they are well loaded, be sure and don't misfire."

6.

Then down into the cabin straightway we did repair,
And to our sad misfortune, few arms could we find there;
We only found six pistols, a gun and two small swords,
And in short time we did agree; "Blow her up!" was the word.

7.

Our powder we got ready, and gun-room open lay,
Our souls we did commit to God, prepared for a watery grave.
We then informed our Captain, saying, "Ready now are we;"
He says, "The signal I will give; it shall be, 'Follow me.' "

8.

All this time upon the quarterdeck, poor man was forced to stand,
With twelve of those cursed savages, with knives all in their hands,
Till one of those bloodthirsty hounds, he made a spring below,
And then he sang out, "Follow me!", and after him did go.

9.

Then with what few firearms we had, we rushed on deck amain,
And by our being resolute, our quarterdeck we gained.
Soon as we gained our arm-chests, sad slaughter then made we,
And in less than ten minutes, our ship of them was free.

10.

Then we threw overboard the dead that on our deck there lay,
And found we had nobody hurt, to work we went straightway,
The number killed upon our deck that day was sixty good,
And full as many wounded, as soon we understood.

11.

'Twas early the next morning, at the hour of break of day,
We sailed along abreast the town which we came to straightway,
We called all hands to quarters, and at the town did play;
We made them to return what things they'd stolen that day.

12.

I'd have you all take warning and always ready be,
For to suppress those savages of Northwest Amerikay,
For they are so desirous some vessel for to gain
That they will never leave it off till most of them are slain.

13.

And now unto old China we're fastly rolling on,
When we shall drink good punch for which we've suffered
long;
And when the sixteenth day of June around does yearly
come,
We'll drink in commemoration what on that day was done.

14.

And now for to conclude and make an end unto my song,
Success to the Commander of the *Lady Washington!*
Success unto his voyages wherever he may go,
And may death and destruction always attend his foe!

After news spread throughout the mercantile world that sea-otter pelts from the north Pacific coast of North America were highly prized in China, ships under a number of flags came to the northwest coast to engage in the new and lucrative fur trade. The people living along that coast were especially eager to barter the furs for pieces of copper and iron, tools, utensils and cloth. As ships' log-books and other records testify, the early meetings between the traders and the coastal villagers were generally friendly. But as a result of the traders' arrogance and certain cultural factors of which they were ignorant, a state verging on warfare eventually developed. The trans-Pacific traders wished to get as much as they could from each dealing, to the point where they threatened villages with cannon and gunfire and held village leaders as prisoners to extort the largest number of furs at the lowest prices. In this the traders were not easily challenged. On the other side of this unequal conflict, coastal villagers on occasion pilfered various goods, such as clothing, left open to their eyes and hands. The reaction of the traders was not untypical of European practices of the day; a person caught stealing would be flogged and forced to return the goods.

On one occasion, two village leaders, one of whom was named Koyah, were seized after some of their people removed drying clothing from a trade ship, the *Lady Washington.* The ship's captain, John Kendrick, had them bound and placed each with a leg clamped in a gun carriage from which the cannon had been removed. One account of the event states that Kendrick "whipped [Koyah], painted his face and cut off his hair." He further threatened to kill them if the store goods were not returned. But even when Koyah's people restored the goods, Kendrick held the chiefs prisoner until all the village's furs were turned over to him at his own price. Koyah's humiliation at Kendrick's hands had disastrous results. To regain his lost prestige, he had either to revenge himself dramatically or, in keeping with the principles of the "potlatch," distribute much wealth—or both. When Kendrick again came to trade at the village, Koyah recognized him and tried to capture his ship. "The Bold Northwestman" relates what then took place. The song title refers to the "heroic" Captain Kendrick, and the story is as seen through the eyes of the Boston traders. Indeed, the story follows closely in detail and in phrase its recording in John Bartlett's manuscript journal, in his entry at the port of Macao for December, 1791. It would seem that Bartlett had the story from the member of the crew who made the ballad, or that the ballad-maker

Map of Haida villages showing Ninstints (after Wilson Duff).

had seen Bartlett's handwritten account. Tradition is that a crew-member composed the ballad.

The events took place in June, 1791 at the village of Ninstints, Anthony Island, on Houston Stewart Channel on the southwest coast of the Queen Charlotte Islands. The name of the chief was written in many ways by the Boston traders, one being Koyah or Coyah. Koyah's exploits as he attempted to regain his status as a great leader included the capture of two ships, but he was not heard of after 1795 when he unsuccessfully tried to take a third. Captain Kendrick's ship the sloop *Lady Washington* left Boston in 1787 with the brig *Columbia* to become the first American ships to join the sea-otter trade. Kendrick began the trading expedition as master of the *Columbia* but sold the *Washington* to himself and became a private adventurer. Neither he nor his ship returned to Boston, he being accidentally killed in the Hawaiian Islands.

The ballad comes down to us in three ways: the first, in oral tradition where two variants were preserved in New Brunswick and Maine to be collected around 1930 (the New Brunswick tune is used here); the second, in a New Brunswick manuscript; the third, in four broadsides or songsheets, the latest of which was printed in Boston in the 1830's, some forty-five years after the events. In the first stanza the ballad probably read originally as "in Coyah's harbour lay." In the later broadsides this has been corrupted to "decoyed as she lay," but in the New Brunswick oral tradition at least a semblance was retained as "in Coyote's harbour lay."

Watercolor from title page of First Mate Robert Haswell's log of the Columbia, *begun as the ship left Boston in September, 1787. The smaller ship is the sloop* Washington *or Lady Washington,* to use her full name.

Massachusetts Historical Society

2

Resolution *and* Discovery *in Nootka Sound 1778*

The Poor Armourer Boy

No thrush that e'er pip'd its sweet note from the thorn Was more live-ly than I, or more free, 'Till lur'd by false col-ours, in life's bloom-ing morn I tempt-ed my for-tune at sea. My fath-er he wept as his bless-ing he gave, When I left him my time to em-ploy In clim-ates re-mote on the rude o-cean wave, Be-ing but a poor Ar-mour-er Boy.

1.

No thrush that e'er pip'd its sweet note from the thorn
Was more lively than I, or more free,
'Till lur'd by false colours, in life's blooming morn
I tempted my fortune at sea.
My father he wept as his blessing he gave,
When I left him "my time to employ"
In climates remote on the rude ocean wave,
Being but a poor Armourer Boy.

2.

Whilst amidst each new scene these "maxims of old"
Upheld me when grief did oppress;
That a fair reputation is better than gold,
And courage will conquer distress:
"So contented I brav'd the rude storm, dry or wet,
Buoy'd up with hopes" light painted toy,
In thinking that Fortune would certainly yet
Deign to smile on the Armourer Boy.

3.

With our ship, on return, with riches full fraught,
We hop'd soon for Boston to steer,
My heart it with ecstacy leap'd at the thought,
"My eyes dropp'd through pleasure a tear."
"But, alas! adverse fate so hard" and untrue
"Did all these gay prospects destroy,"
For burn'd was our ship and murder'd our crew,
And wounded the Armourer Boy.

4.

For a long time in pain and sickness I pin'd,
With no one to feel for my woe,
No mother, my wounds, as she sooth'd me, to bind,
No sister her aid to bestow!
By savages fierce for years held a slave,
Did affliction my poor heart annoy,
Till Hope dropp'd her anchor at last on the grave
As the *birth* of the Armourer Boy.   *(old spelling of "berth")*

5.

From slav'ry escap'd, I, joyful once more
Hail'd a civiliz'd land, but alone
And a stranger was I on a far-distant shore
From that which my childhood had known.
"If such be life's fate, with emotion I cried,"
Of sorrow so great the alloy;
"Heaven grant the sole blessing that ne'er is denied,"
To the friendless Poor Armourer Boy!

Note:
The text is as it appears on Jewitt's broadside. The quotation marks are puzzling but suggest that the phrases thus marked were taken from "The Poor Cabin Boy," the song which Jewitt's song imitates.

The ballad "The Poor Armourer Boy" has its origins in the "adventures and sufferings" of a young Englishman, John R. Jewitt, who was captive of the Indians of Nootka Sound, Vancouver Island, for over two years from 1803 to 1805. The song, which has a literary flavor, was likely written in 1815 by Richard Alsop, a minor writer of the day in Connecticut where Jewitt eventually settled after his rescue. Alsop unquestionably wrote a book-length story on Jewitt's experiences, *Narrative of the Adventures and Sufferings of John R. Jewitt.* For this he interviewed Jewitt and used the autobiographical form and style of Defoe's *Robinson Crusoe.* The Alsop narrative was a very popular book which went through many editions, but it made Jewitt a more heroic figure than he really was. A straightforward account of incidents during the captivity can be found in Jewitt's Nootkan journal which was published in Boston in 1807. The ballad, like Alsop's book, is designed to affect an audience rather than simply present Jewitt's experience. Within its narrow scope, the song attempts to evoke pity for a young man almost broken in body and spirit by a harrowing experience. After his rescue, Jewitt is portrayed as friendless in a foreign land with nothing to hope for but death.

In contrast to the picture given in the song, Jewitt appears to have been welcomed in his newly adopted home. Not only was his journal immediately published, but it was not long before he was married. By the time the song was printed in 1815 he had a family of several children. Why then did Jewitt have such a song composed? He may well have intended it to be a broadside companion to the Alsop *Narrative*, which was also first published in 1815. Jewitt sold the book on the streets of towns in the northeastern United States between 1815 and his death in 1821. Jewitt also sang the song as the curtain closer for the "historical melodrama," *The Amourer's Escape,* presented in Philadelphia in 1817, in which he was both director and leading actor.

In the years around 1800 the American trade for sea otter pelts was thriving. This trade can be represented by a triangle, the points being New England, the north Pacific coast of North America, and China. John Jewitt, aged 19, saw in this trade a chance to make the money needed to give him a good start as an immigrant to New York City. Although he had some formal schooling, the trade of blacksmith, which he had learned from his father, was where he placed his hope. In the late summer of 1802 when the American ship *Boston* was taking on trade materials in the North Sea port of Hull, Jewitt signed on as ship's armourer or blacksmith.

When the *Boston* anchored in Nootka Sound in March, 1803, the ship's company of twenty-seven were of course unaware that the village leaders had already determined to massacre them and take the vessel and its cargo as booty. These men of Nootka, whose chief was Maquinna, had from the time of Captain James Cook's first visit twenty-five years earlier traded with Spanish, English and American adventurers. Their bloody decision was brought about by the fact that again and again the Nootkans had been outraged and humiliated by the traders. Some of their chiefs had been killed, their village plundered and their people slaughtered with little provocation. A state bordering on warfare had developed. In revenge for acts done at different times by men of different ships, Maquinna and his fellow chiefs determined to capture the next ship to enter their waters. That ship chanced to be the *Boston.*

The Nootkan's plan was a success. By killing twenty-five of the crew they expiated the earlier murders of Nootkan people. Maquinna's prestige among his own and neighboring peoples rose as he distributed his prize of muskets, gunpowder, shot, and cloth. The two crew members who survived also added to Maquinna's wealth. Jewitt, although cut on the head, was spared by Maquinna who recognized him as the armourer, the man who could work metals, the blacksmith and gunsmith. The other man, John Thompson, an American from Philadelphia, avoided the massacre by hiding below decks where he was at work as the ship's sailmaker. Both were made part of Maquinna's household and worked primarily at their trades. Jewitt made daggers, harpoons, fish hooks and copper rings; Thompson made sails for canoes, clothing and whaling lines, and helped with the iron work. Because they were valued craftsmen, Maquinna gave them protection from villagers who harrassed them at times and would have killed them. In the subsistence fishing and whaling economy, they faced the same hardships as the other villagers and were occasionally very hungry.

The forty-year-old Thompson regularly prayed for deliverance from a situation for which he had only antipathy. The youthful Jewitt, on the other hand, although joining Thompson in his prayers, gradually adapted himself to much of Nootkan life. In the summer of 1804 Jewitt tells us that he is able at last to enjoy the common village food. Some entries in the journal show that he had warmed to his captors as people. Maquinna hoped Jewitt would choose to stay with him and

The captive—forehead scarred—holding a copy of the partly fictitious narrative of his experiences.

The captor—regarded as an enlightened leader and dubbed by B.C. historian B.A. McKelvie "Maquinna the Magnificent."

THE POOR ARMOURER BOY,

A SONG.

Imitated from the "POOR CABIN BOY," of Dibdin, and adapted to the case of John R. Jewitt, a native of Boston, in Great-Britain, the only survivor of the crew of the ship Boston, of Boston in New-England, who with the captain and officers were cruelly massacred by the savages on the North-West coast of America.

TUNE—"*The Poor Cabin Boy.*"

NO thrush that e'er pip'd its sweet note from the thorn
   Was more lively than I, or more free,
"Till lur'd by false colours, in life's blooming morn
   I tempted my fortune at sea.
My father he wept as his blessing he gave,
   When I lash him " my time to employ"
In climates remote on the rude ocean wave,
   Being but a poor Armourer Boy.

Whilst amidst each new scene these "maxims of old"
   Upheld me when grief did oppress ;
That a fair reputation is better than gold,
   And courage will conquer distress :
" So contented I brav'd the rude storm, dry or wet,
   Buoy'd up with hopes' light painted toy,
In thinking that Fortune would certainly yet
   Deign to smile on the Armourer Boy.

With our ship, on return, with riches full fraught,
   We hop'd soon for Boston to steer,
" My heart it with exstacy leap'd at the thought,
   " My eyes droppi'd through pleasure a tear."
" But, alas ! adverse fate so hard" and untrue
   " Did all these gay prospects destroy,
For burn'd was our ship and murder'd our crew,
   And wounded the Armourer Boy.

For a long time in pain and sickness I pin'd,
   With no one to feel for my woe,
No mother, my wounds, as she sooth'd me, to bind,
   No sister her aid to bestow !
By savages fierce for years held a slave,
   Did affliction my poor heart annoy,
Till Hope dropp'd her anchor at last on the grave
   As the birth of the Armourer Boy.

From slav'ry escap'd, I, joyful, once more
   Hail'd a civiliz'd land, but alone
And a stranger was I on a far-distant shore
   From that which my childhood had known.
" If such be life's fate, with emotion I cried,"
   Of sorrow so great the alloy ;
" Heaven grant the sole blessing that ne'er is denied,"
   To the friendless Poor Armourer Boy !

One of two known slightly differing broadsides of the song John R. Jewitt sang and sold in the northeastern United States after its publication in 1815.

become truly one of his people. He came to treat him in some ways as an adopted son. In September, 1804, he arranged a marriage for him, paying the bride price. Following the marriage Jewitt was ordered to give up his European habit of dress and go naked except for a woven cedar blanket, as was the Nootkan custom. Had Jewitt and Thompson been regularly engaged in arduous physical activity as were the whalers and fishermen, they might not have suffered so much from the cold. Thompson was sickly all of the following winter, and in March 1805, Jewitt was unwell for a few weeks. During his illness Jewitt prevailed upon Maquinna to permit him to separate from his wife, who was by then five months pregnant.

Trade ships had avoided Nootka Sound after the *Boston's* capture, but Jewitt had sent by hand of visitors from other villages up and down the coast many letters appealing for help for Thompson and himself. In July 1805, one of the letters brought a trade ship to their rescue. Two years later in 1807, after sailing to China, Jewitt finally completed the trade triangle at the New England port of Boston.

As can be seen from the foregoing overview, "The Poor Armourer Boy" does not tell Jewitt's actual story. Instead it follows the formula of a popular song of sentiment with stereotyped hero and villain, dashed hopes, and narrow escape. Once Jewitt had decided to exploit his experiences for a livelihood, it was natural that he should commission a song of his own. He had enjoyed a reputation as a singer during his teens, and according to one report he had sung and recited in his own language for the Nootkan people.

The tune he used for the song is not known, but since it was intended to be a Dibdin-like song, a search for a model has been made through Charles Dibdin's ninety-nine sea songs. There is no record that Charles Dibdin or the other two Dibdin authors wrote a song titled "The Poor Cabin Boy," which Jewitt's broadside purports is the model of his song. Only one of Dibdin's sea songs, "Jack's Fidelity," has a verse form matching "The Poor Armourer Boy," but its tune is unsuitable in mood and cannot be handled by an untrained voice. The verse form was not uncommon around 1815. It is found a century earlier in D'Urfey's *Pills to Purge Melancholy* and several examples, including "Believe Me, If All Those Endearing Young Charms," written in 1808, are in Thomas Moore's *Irish Melodies*. It is likely that the model was a song attributed to Dibdin and now lost. It could well have been a song of the same genre as this anonymous untitled piece published in *The Sailor's Medley* in Philadelphia in 1800:

Oh, think on my fate! once I freedom enjoy'd,
Was as happy as happy could be,
But pleasure is fled! even hope is destroy'd,
A captive alas! on the sea.
I was ta'en by the foe, 'twas the fiat of fate,
To tear me from her I adore,
When thought brings to mind my once happy estate,
I sigh, while I tug at the oar.

The hero in this song scorns the lash and, at the end of the third stanza, despairs of ever seeing his love again and dies "at the oar." Lacking such a universal theme as dying for love, Jewitt's song must have depended for success on his own presentation and appearance, his scar clearly visible on his forehead. It did not survive in oral tradition as did the genuine ballad, "The Bold Northwestman," but two copies of the broadside have come down to us.

3

Annexation

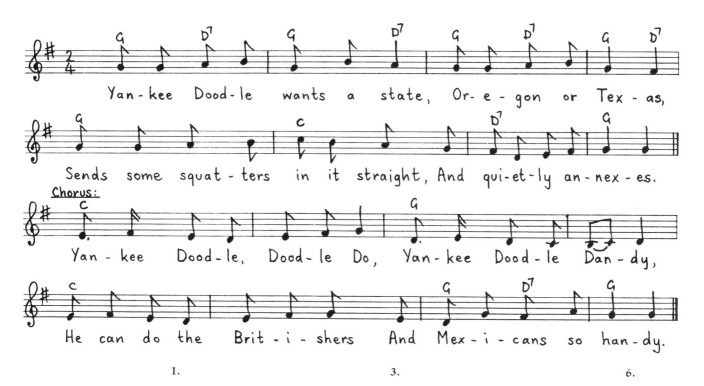

1.

Yankee Doodle wants a state,
Oregon or Texas,
Sends some squatters in it straight,
And quietly annexes.

Chorus

Yankee Doodle, Doodle Do,
Yankee Doodle Dandy,
He can do the Britishers
And Mexicans so handy.

2.

Canada's a pleasant place,
So is California;
Yankee Doodle wants them all,
But first he cribs a corner.

3.

General Cass he made a speech,
Archer called it splutter,
He swore he'd tear the British Jack
And wipe it in the gutter.

4.

Jabez Honan took an oath,
By the living Jingo!
Cuba soon shall be our own
And so shall Saint Domingo.

5.

Yankee has some public works,
Well he may parade them,
English money paid for all,
And Irish labour made them.

6.

Then hey for Yankee Doodle's luck,
And for Annexation;
Hey for Yankee Doodle's pluck
And for Repudiation.

Last chorus

Yankee Doodle, Doodle Do,
Yankee Doodle Dandy,
And hey for Sherry Cobbler too,
Mint julep and peach brandy.

17

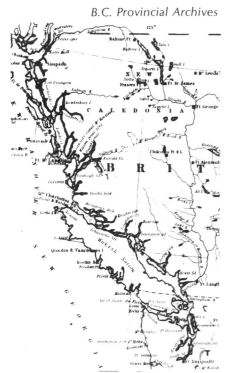

U.S. map of 1838 showing boundary extending west from plains and cutting through Vancouver Island.

"Annexation 1846" was written in London in 1846, a short time before Great Britain and the United States settled on the boundary through the region they had jointly occupied west of the Rocky Mountains. The song documents, howbeit satirically, a simplified story of the personalities and events of 1845-6 as seen from England. It introduces leading political figures of the day: President James K. Polk and General Lewis Cass, western Democrats filled with expansionist zeal; and Senator William S. Archer of the Whigs, who opposed Polk's war policies. The song begins with an explanation of how expansionist policies worked in practice. Americans moving west spread the southern plantation system in the lands adjacent to the Gulf of Mexico; others moved into the southwest as cattlemen. They settled in sufficient numbers to create their own government inside Mexican territory and then to invite annexation of the area by their home government. The song is prophetic, for the annexation from Mexico of Texas in 1845 was followed by Mexico's ceding California to the United States in 1848.

The song sees the same pattern in the Pacific northwest. There American settlers took up land in the Columbia River region. They were called "squatters" by the Hudson's Bay Company which claimed ownership of some of the settlers' farmland. While American settlers were beginning to supplant the Hudson's Bay Company in the valleys of the lower Columbia, United States expansionist leaders were determined to bring the area under the American flag. Polk and Cass in the 1844 presidential election campaign demanded, by right of arms if necessary, annexation of the whole territory west of the Rockies occupied by the British company. Today this area includes Oregon, Washington, Idaho, part of Montana, and most of British Columbia. The writer of the song sees this as an attempt to "crib" a corner of "Canada." His "Canada" was apparently synonymous with all of British North America. He no doubt recalled that in 1812 American expansionists with continental ambitions had tried to annex a large corner of Upper Canada. The song's reference to Cuba sprang from talk at the time of American annexation of the Spanish-held island. This was in part an application of the Monroe Doctrine, but more an opportunity for the extension of American slave territory. For audiences in the 1840's the mention in the last chorus of "mint julep" readily conjured up the image of a southern slave owner. Brother Jonathan, the cartoon predecessor of Uncle Sam, was often pictured with a mint julep in one hand and a slave whip in the other.

The reference to British money paying for American public works was topical in London in 1846 since many British investors were smarting under their losses in the American bond market. Many American states had financed canals, highways and their early railroads by issuing or guaranteeing bonds the bulk of which were sold to British capitalists. In contrast to the happy beginnings in the 1820's when British capital financed New York State's Erie Canal, many states by the early 1840's were nearly bankrupt. They had their public works but never did repay their loans. A number of states openly declared they would not honor these bonds. About 1840 the word "repudiation" was given a new meaning to indicate a state's refusal to discharge its public debt. In the last chorus of the song, "repudiation" has this overtone as well as signifying a strong rejection of Polk's annexation threats.

The Territory, The Boundary, The Conflict

The story of the dispute reaches back through the years of the inland and coastal fur trade to the American, British, Spanish and Russian exploration of the coast. Specific British-American negotiations referring to the Pacific northwest started in 1818, four years after the War of 1812 ended. At that time the two nations made a number of agreements and signed a Convention of Commerce to ease tensions between them and promote continental peace. One joint decision was that the 49th parallel should be the boundary from the Lake of the Woods to the Rocky Mountains. Since they could not settle on a boundary for the territory between the Rockies and the Pacific, they agreed to share its use for a period of ten years. In 1827 they again agreed to share its use, but made a provision that either party could end the agreement on a year's notice. In 1846 after over twenty-five years of joint occupation, diplomatic exchanges and negotiations, Great Britain and the United States finally decided on the western boundary. During this time economic and political factors had so evolved that Great Britain gave up many of her territorial claims in the face of American pressure. She acceded to all United States demands except that Vancouver Island be divided. The boundary agreed to simply extend the 49th parallel to the coast and then passed south of Vancouver Island through the Strait of Juan de Fuca. The ambiguous boundary through the Gulf and San Juan Islands was finally made clear in the Treaty of Washington in 1871.

When the territory thus divided was first considered by the two nations in 1818, it was vaguely defined. By 1825 it had become clearly marked through bilateral treaties between the United States and Spain, the United States and Russia, and Great Britain and Russia. It extended from the Pacific Ocean to the Rocky Mountains and ran north from 42° to 54° 40′ North Latitude. The whole of it came within a region called "Columbia" on a British map of 1832. The United States gave the area the name "Oregon Country" or just "Oregon."

Polk, a Western Democrat from Tennessee, reflected the expansionist spirit which a generation earlier in 1812 had produced the militant drive for the United States' attempt to annex Upper Canada. By 1844 American expansionists confined their dreams to the possible and directed their energies southwest to the Mexican territories of Texas and California and west to the Oregon Country. After Polk was elected President using the slogan "Fifty-four forty or fight!", a Democrat journalist paraphrased a key statement

Brother Jonathan, cartoon precursor of Uncle Sam, was used to reflect English views of pre-Civil-War America.

in his inaugural address, giving the expansionists a new catch phrase:

> Our manifest destiny is to spread over the continent allotted by Providence for the free development of our yearly multiplying millions.

Pursuing this "manifest destiny," Polk annexed Texas, prepared for war against Mexico and gave Great Britain notice that the agreement to share the Oregon Country was to terminate. Faced with the aggressive temper of the United States, Great Britain was pleased to get the concession of an undivided Vancouver Island, without the gamble and cost of a war of "honour" for the boundary which now separates the south of British Columbia from the United States.

In order to understand why the British in 1846 were less motivated than the Americans to hold the Columbia River basin, one must see the British involvement in the Pacific northwest to that time as but one of her many business ventures around the world. After British explorers by land and sea found no northwest passage, her merchants took part in the profitable trade of sea otter pelts. By 1811 the North West Company of Montreal was pressing west into the Columbia River basin, the last large resource of beaver pelts on the continent. By 1818, when the issue of the boundary was raised, Britain did not wish this trade disrupted and agreed to share access to the region with American fur traders. The Hudson's Bay Company, which amalgamated with the "Nor'westers" in 1821, soon dominated trade in the area. By the late 1830's there was such a marked decline of furs that British interest in the region lessened. Once the animals had become scarce, there was no immediately profitable resource to keep the British in the area.

The Americans, on the other hand, although they initially came in the interest of the fur trade, were arriving as settlers by the 1830's. American expansionists saw in such potential farmlands as the Willamette Valley a new frontier. The Hudson's Bay Company did engage in agriculture as a facet of their fur trade enterprise, but the Company was unenthusiastic about large scale settlement. Agricultural settlement would only hasten the decline of the fur resource. Thus for economic reasons the British fur trade interests opposed American migration into the Pacific northwest. But they had no power to stop it. Those with a vision of a new frontier prevailed. The narrow concern of Hudson's Bay Company was still in evidence years later on Vancouver Island where the Company had agreed to foster a colony. Settlement was slow and always in terms of Company welfare with no view to creating an independent community.

Victoria, Vancouver Island

Victoria c. 1869

4

Chief Douglas's Daughter

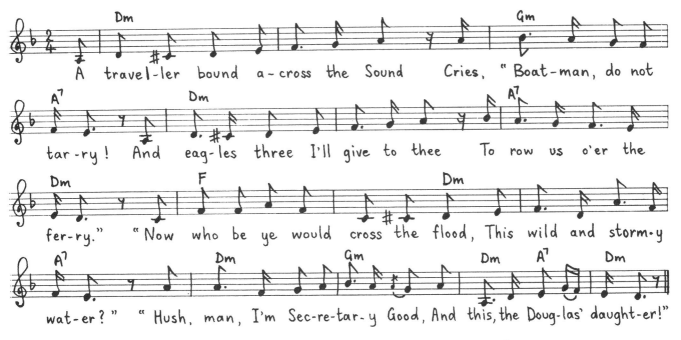

A travel-ler bound a-cross the Sound Cries, "Boat-man, do not tar-ry! And eag-les three I'll give to thee To row us o'er the fer-ry." "Now who be ye would cross the flood, This wild and storm-y wat-er?" "Hush, man, I'm Sec-re-tar-y Good, And this, the Doug-las' daught-er!"

1.

A traveler bound across the Sound
Cries, "Boatman, do not tarry!
And Eagles three I'll give to thee
To row us o'er the ferry."
"Now who be ye would cross the flood,
This wild and stormy water?"
"Hush, man, I'm Secretary Good,
And this, the Douglas's daughter!"

2.

"Three days ago I asked her hand
The chieftain bade me dry up!
And should he find me where I stand,
He'd bung my other eye up!"
Out spake the hardy boatman then,
"Come on, my buck, I'm ready!
It is not for your Eagles bright,
But for your plucky lady!"

3.

"And by my word, the bonny bird
Shall now find Fortune's frowns end;
So though the waves are raging white,
I'll row you to Port Townsend!"
The chieftain after dinner sat,
Sipping his rum and water;
"But where's my Alice? Where's my pet?
My daughter! Oh, my daughter!"

4.

He to his castle window hied,
He gazed out over the trellis,
And in a schooner, bobbing round,
Espied his daughter Alice.
"What ho, my gallant Drake!" cried he,
"Quick to my house restore her;
Your sire of old explored yon coast,
Go catch me yon *Explorer!*"

5.

"Now haste, love, haste!" the lady cried,
"Oh, Charlie dear, I'd rather
Get married on the other side
Then taken back to father!
And, by the rood, my sight is good,
Yon sternmost schooner, stuck in,
I'm sure I see the odious Drake;
I hope he'll get a ducking."

6.

The night fell dark; the lovers' barque
By Cupid's aid befriended,
The land was made, the J.P. paid,
And all their troubles ended.
And in the morn, the gallant Drake,
While brailing up his spanker,
Espied the lovers in a bay,
Quite cosily at anchor.

7.

Quick alongside impetuously
He boarded in a passion,
"Come back!" said he; "I shan't!" said she—
"We're married Yankee fashion."
"Ah! Is it so?" cried Drake: "Alas!
None destiny can master;
Since Jonathan has tied you fast,
John Bull must tie you faster!

8.

"Come back!—It is your sire's command,
Though all our plans you've blighted,
And since you've been united here,
You'll there be re-united."
Back then they came and in the church
(Both Pa and Ma consenting)
The pair were wed—went home to bed,
And Drake was left lamenting.

If comedy depends on character's being subjected to minor pain, to frustration, then the scene was set for a laugh when Governor James Douglas of Vancouver Island tried to stop the marriage between his daughter Alice and his private secretary Charles Good. The main events in the story took place from August 30 to September 2, 1861. There is no doubt from the tone of newspaper reports and other documents left to us that many people in colonial Victoria found it all very funny. In actuality it was a poignant family drama with romantic and, perhaps, tragic overtones. The public view of what happened would have made a comic opera. The hero is a penniless but ambitious government clerk in the service of a small kingdom; the heroine is the daughter of the rigid and autocratic ruler. When the hero asks for the princess' hand in marriage, the potentate replies by punching him in the eye. The suitor, undaunted, contrives a midnight elopement by sea to a neighbouring country out of reach of the father's authority. The drama heightens as the potentate dispatches another ship in pursuit. A sub-plot appears, for the man chosen to lead the interception has also shown interest in the princess; as a young and promising lawyer he is much more to the father's liking. Alas! all devices are too late, for before they are overtaken the lovers are married by an official on the foreign shore. With a promise of the father's forgiveness they return to their own land triumphant in each other's eyes. But the authority of the family and of the state is finally re-established when four days after the elopement they are married a second time in all solemnity in the presence of the bride's parents by the most venerable churchman in the little kingdom.

The characters in this scenario in order of appearance are: Charles Good, Alice Douglas, Governor James Douglas, W.M.T. Drake, Mrs. Amelia Douglas, Rev. Edward Cridge. To describe these people as three-dimensional persons requires the biographer's art, but a few words about each, where possible from people who knew them, should help place us in Victoria, 1861, and also put the scene in an historical perspective.

"the hero"

Charles Good ("the hero"): The most revealing document on Charles Good is the following excerpt, dated October 9, 1859, from the diary of Charles Wilson, secretary of the British Boundary Commission which was surveying and mapping the border between British Columbia and the American territories.

> The Governor paid me a visit the other day, came down just as I was getting up about half past six, Good attending in his capacity of private Secretary... We rode about 40 miles... poor Good... was dreadfully stiff and sore, the old Governor... enjoyed himself greatly. Good has been one of the lucky men who have drawn a prize in the lottery of this colony; he was first appointed clerk in the colonial secretary's office & is now the Governor's private secretary; he is not a bad sort of fellow on the whole, but utterly selfish in all public matters & is not at all liked in his present capacity. From his conversation I should say he had been a notable tuft hunter at Oxford & spent everything he had & a great deal more in trying to keep up with the swells, & is something of the same sort here.

Good was in fact a Cambridge graduate. Subsequent to his marriage to Alice, he became clerk to the Legislative Assembly, then Deputy Provincial Secretary. Whether Good's romantic determination was in truth largely a desire for a career and financial solvency we can only guess; he certainly became part of the family-company-compact which dominated early Victoria. His marriage did not last very many years; he returned to England alone in 1877.

Alice Douglas ("the heroine"): At the time of elopement, Alice was seventeen. She was born at Fort Vancouver and came with the family to Fort Victoria in 1849 when the Hudson's Bay Company headquarters was moved from the lower Columbia River to Vancouver Island. Until she was seven, Alice lived in the secluded women's quarters of a typical stockaded fort. In 1851 the family moved into the large house her father built when he became Governor of the Crown Colony of Vancouver Island.

Alice was one of the four Douglas daughters who married men who were or who became part of the Victoria establishment. Her marriage to Charles Good ended after some years in separation and divorce. She then married the Baron de Wiederhold of San Francisco, where she made her home with the children of both marriages.

Governor James Douglas ("the irate father"): In the Hudson's Bay Company records he is described as a "West Indian" or "Scotch West Indian". He was born in 1803 in Demerara, British Guiana, one of three children from a relationship between his father and a Creole woman. His father's family were in the Glasgow sugar business and had plantations in the West Indies. After schooling in Scotland, at the age of sixteen he joined the North West Company as clerk. When the Nor'westers merged with the Hudson's Bay Company, he continued in the fur trade and by 1840 had achieved the rank of Chief Factor. After the Oregon Country boundary settlement he was placed in charge of the Western Department of the Hudson's Bay Company, with headquarters in Victoria. After the Hudson's Bay Company undertook the responsibility of colonizing Vancouver Island, he became in 1851 the Colony's second Governor. During the 1858 gold rush on the Fraser River he asserted British territorial rights north of

"the heroine"

"the irate father"

the 49th parallel and was appointed Governor of the new mainland Colony of British Columbia.

Although he slowly transferred his loyalty from the Hudson's Bay Company to the British Crown, he always did his duty as he saw it. Scrupulous in matters of fairness before the law, Douglas was nevertheless through his fur-trade experience and by temperament no democrat. Where he made the law, his decisions were oligarchic and set the direction of government and business in the region for the rest of the century — despite the coming of representative government. As Governor he became through choice and partly by luck the center of an effective government clique. His Colonial Council were old fur-trade colleagues, and all major appointments were either Hudson's Bay Company or family connections. He early appointed his brother-in-law, John Cameron, whom he brought with his sister from Demerara, Chief Justice of Vancouver Island. Douglas made his niece's husband. W.A.G. Young, Colonial Secretary of Vancouver Island and later of mainland British Columbia. Douglas's successor as head of the Western Department of the Hudson's Bay Company, A.G. Dallas, married Douglas's daughter Jane. The Hudson's Bay Company surgeon, Dr. J.S. Helmcken, wedded to Douglas's daughter Cecilia, became the first Speaker of the Legislative Assembly of Vancouver Island. When Judge Matthew Begbie's private secretary, Arthur Bushby, married Douglas's daughter Agnes, he was appointed Registrar General of the mainland Colony. And then there was Charles Good and Alice. This list deals merely with Douglas's family, but it exemplifies the character of the establishment of the period and reflects the values that produced first the "Company Colony" and in time what has been called the "Company Province."

Douglas and his clique were not without active critics. Editors Amor de Cosmos with his *Colonist* and John Robson with his *British Columbian* in New Westminster both saw themselves as voices of liberty, fighting for political reforms already won in the eastern colonies which were soon to become provinces of the Dominion of Canada.

Douglas's character is especially revealed in these observations by people who knew him. In his "Character Book" of 1832, Governor Simpson (head of the Hudson's Bay Company) described Douglas as

> a stout powerful active man of good conduct and respectable abilities—tolerably well educated, expresses himself clearly on paper, understands our Counting House business and is an excellent Trader. Well qualified for any Service requiring bodily exertion, firmness of mind and the exercise of sound judgment, but furiously violent when roused. Has every reason to look forward to early promotion and is a likely man to fill a place at our Council board in time....

In 1859 a clerk in the colonial government gave Douglas the nickname "Old Square-toes". In 1868 John Tod, pensioner of the Hudson's Bay Company and one of the members of the early Colonial Council wrote in a letter:

> I had a long chat the other day with our friend Douglas (now Sir James) ever stiff and formal as in times past, qualities which, from long habit he could not now lay aside, if he would, and probably ought not, if he could....

24

John Tod's "probably ought not" suggests that, on reflection and taking the circumstances as they were, he approved Douglas's role in the great changes of the twenty preceding years. Douglas's strong hand on the helm during the most critical of those years has caused many people to acknowledge him as "The Father of British Columbia."

W.M.T. Drake ("the pursuer"): A contemporary, J.R. Anderson, in retelling the elopement story years later in his memoirs, lightly disguises the names of the characters. Charles Good becomes "Mr. Bad." He describes Drake's part thus:

> A young and promising lawyer whom I shall call Mr. Duck, who, it was currently reported had serious intentions regarding the hand of the damsel, was hurriedly summoned and... was despatched after the fugitives.. (Ms in B.C. Provincial Archives)

W.M.T. Drake was early the Hudson's Bay Company solicitor. He continued in his legal career and from 1868 to 1870 was a representative for Victoria City on the Legislative Council of the combined colony of British Columbia.

Mrs. Amelia Douglas ("the mother"): She was the daughter of Hudson's Bay Company Chief Factor William Connolly and his Cree Indian wife. James Douglas and she were married "according to the custom of the country" at Fort St. James in 1828. At the fort she was called "Little Snowbird" because of her small size and fair skin. She also had auburn hair and grey eyes. Although she was only sixteen years old when she was married, she must have been a spirited young woman for about three months later she saved her husband's life when he became the object of revenge for his part in the brutal execution of a Stuart Lake Indian who was accused of murdering two Hudson's Bay Company servants. She was carrying their first baby when Douglas was transferred to Fort Vancouver the next year; but before she joined him there in 1830, the baby died. At Fort Vancouver over the next nineteen years Douglas rose in the service of the Company from Accountant to Chief Factor, and Amelia gave birth to ten more children. Four of these, all daughters, survived through infancy to adulthood. Amelia and her children lived with other women of the fort in quarters removed from "Bachelor's Hall" and the mess hall where all the company officers ate. The women took no part in the social life of the fort.

Little by little Amelia had the ways of English society impressed upon her. For example, although she was already married, in 1836 at the rather unpleasant insistence of the new Company Chaplain and his wife, a number of couples at Fort Vancouver, including the Douglases, went through the Church of England form of Christian marriage. Amelia eventually had her own home, but not until two years after moving to Fort Victoria, when the Douglas family moved into a conventional two-story house. There she gave birth to a boy and another girl. She saw to the many matters of a large household, tending the chickens and preparing jellies, jams and vegetables for winter. She was a loving mother and was especially remembered for her story-telling. Douglas's letters reveal a deep and abiding affection for her. He showed this by not forcing on her ritual social duties conventional to a Governor's wife. She did, however, receive many visitors and took part in a limited way in social events in the growing

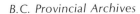

"the pursuer"

"the mother"

town. She went to the theatre now and then. When she became Lady Douglas in 1864 on Douglas's retirement and conferral of knighthood, she continued active for many years. While Sir James travelled to Europe many times, she stayed in Victoria. Except for one period in the late 1860's she was in good health, driving out several times a week and picnicking often. Douglas said of her in those years that she kept active, believing "that nothing could go on prosperously without her close attendance." Marion B. Smith, in her biographical essay "The Lady Nobody Knows" in *British Columbia: A Centennial Anthology*, made an epitaph for Amelia from words written and said about her by Douglas, her children and grandchildren: "The quaint songs and the sweet voice, the winter gloaming and bright fire... won all hearts with her kindness... especially to poor people... she told such wonderful stories... beautiful legends... darling, good Mama." She died in 1890.

Rev. Edward Cridge ("the churchman"): Victoria was early a city of churches. In 1861 five churches served the six hundred permanent residents. Rev. Cridge was at that time the longest resident minister. He had been brought to Vancouver Island as Hudson's Bay Company Chaplain in 1854 and was almost immediately made Colonial Chaplain with the approval of the Colonial Office in London. He became the center of controversy twice in the next twenty years.

The first occasion was when his appointment came up before the new Legislative Assembly for renewal in 1859. Since a reappointment meant the provision of money, the members of the Assembly no doubt were inclined to give the matter a hard look. But the issue they raised was much more statesmanlike than that; they deferred consideration of the matter until a larger more representative Assembly was formed, for the real issue was one of the union or separation of Church and State. Dr. Helmcken, the Speaker of the Assembly, was the lone voice in support of a permanent appointment. Amor de Cosmos came out in his *Colonist* editorial strongly against an Established Church. It was Douglas's intention to place the Church of England in a preferred position in the two Crown Colonies; but the matter was left with churches relying for support on their own institutions and their congregations.

The second controversy came in 1873. Rev. Cridge, now a Dean for many years, disagreed with his bishop who wished to introduce more ritual into the service as in High Church practice. After losing a Supreme Court battle over authority, Cridge led his supporters out of the congregation. Sir James Douglas gave him land on which he built a new church, the Reformed Episcopal Church. There Cridge continued to follow Low Church practice in which his more evangelical temper could prevail.

The ballad "Chief Douglas's Daughter," in view of the personalities and issues of the time, has a gently satirical strain running through it. If comic opera, then it is Gilbert and Sullivan. The author, whoever he was, took as a model Thomas Campbell's "Lord Ullin's Daughter," written about 1825.

Author Photo

"the churchman"

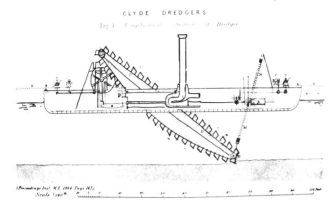

5

The Dredger

Vic-tor-ia town is near-ly caved, Lots scarce-ly worth a

pin there, Be-cause the bot-tom won't fall out And let the ships come

in there. Says Joe D. P. to Am-iede C., "Let's tot the pub-lic

led-ger, And if there's an-y tin to spare, I'll go and buy a dred-ger.

"Oh, the dred-ger, the pret-ty lit-tle dred-ger! A

trip to Eur-ope's just the thing; I'll go and buy a dred-ger."

Author photo   *Author photo*

"Says Joe D.P...   ...to Amie de C."

1.
Victoria town is nearly caved,
Lots scarcely worth a pin there,
Because the bottom won't fall out
And let big ships come in there.
Says Joe D.P. to Amie de C.,
"Let's tot the public ledger,
And if there's any tin to spare,
I'll go and buy a dredger.
  "Oh, the dredger, the pretty little dredger!
  A trip to Europe's just the thing;
  I'll go and buy a dredger."

2.
The dredger came in course of time,
Victorians thought an age it was;
But when at length the thing arrived,
Oh, murder! All the rage it was!
And Joe D.P. and Amie de C.
Most jollily did snigger,
Thinking how they'd make the natives stare,
A-working of their digger.
  Oh, the dredger, the pretty little dredger!
  Alotting rock and swamp is small,
  To building of a dredger.

3.
Such hammering and screwing,
Such polishing and oiling,
At length they got the thing to work,
And set the kettle boiling.
J.D. sat on the safety valve,
D.C. released the wheels,
With rattling chains and hissing steam
They scared the crabs and eels!
  But the dredger, the dirty little dredger,
  The Devil the stone it would bring up,
  Victoria's useless dredger!

4.
The Governor can't tell what to do
With this pretty plaything;
Asks the wisdom of his councilors,
As to making it a paything.
As the thing's no use to anyone,
He can neither sell nor pledge her,
But if he asks me, I'll tell him how
To occupy the dredger.
  Oh, that dredger, that dirty little dredger!
  I've struck a job that exactly suits
  Victoria's useless dredger.

5.
Not a storing ship, as some propose,
For Capital Petitions,
Nor a Lunatic Asylum for
Victoria's politicians,
Nor exhibit her from port to port,
Just like the Bantrie rams, Sir;
Far better, send her to Mud Bay,
And set her digging clams, Sir!
  Oh, this dredger! That great big useless dredger!
  That's a job exactly suits
  Victoria's useless dredger!

When "The Dredger" was written in 1867, Victoria's dredging machine had been shut down for two years. It lay at anchor near the harbor's shoaling south shore at the entrance to James Bay; and there, in view of the town and the legislative buildings or "The Birdcages," as they were called, it was a continuing reminder of the dreams and hopes it had held out for some five years to Victoria's planners, promoters, and real estate speculators.

The song put together in a tight little satire a number of factors in the situation: representative personalities of the old Hudson's Bay Company establishment and the new arrivals, two groups united by their common interest in business and real estate; their naive vision of the dredger as a panacea for the economic slumps which followed the Fraser River and Cariboo gold rushes; the difficulty in adapting the dredging equipment to its task; and the reported incompetence of the superintendent of dredging operations, transferred in the song through caricature to Joseph Despard Pemberton and Amor De Cosmos.

Both Pemberton and De Cosmos had been supporters of the dredger scheme from its beginning and in mid-1865, as members of the Legislative Assembly on Vancouver Island, were in favor of going ahead even though operation costs had been found to greatly exceed the estimates. That the two men still sat in the assembly in 1867 accounts in part for the writer's singling them out, but their backgrounds and their status as landowners must have also influenced him.

Pemberton had joined the Hudson's Bay Company on Vancouver Island in 1851 as Colonial Engineer and Surveyor. Among many tasks, which included road and bridge building, he made the basic land surveys which ably complemented the Admiralty charting of the lower island. In Victoria he laid out the townsite and acquired, according to one account, 1200 acres of land, two hundred of which later became residential lots. When he returned from England in 1864 after purchasing the dredger equipment and finding a bride, he resigned from his government post as Surveyor General to manage his estate.

De Cosmos, on the other hand, was not a large landholder; and he had neither connections with nor love for the Hudson's Bay Company clique. Born William Alexander Smith in Nova Scotia, he came to Victoria in the boom of 1858 by way of California where he had earlier been a gold-rush photographer. He founded the *British Colonist* newspaper and in its editorials fought the colony's family-company compact and championed representative and responsible government. He saw himself as the Joseph Howe of the western shores of British North America. As a real estate holder, he is reported in 1866 to have added to his four Victoria lots by purchasing others sold by the government for unpaid taxes—the result of declining fortunes in Victoria, which at this time had many bankruptcies. Although the colorful De Cosmos was the most reform-minded politician of the decade preceding British Columbia's entering the Canadian federation, he was nonetheless not a disinterested booster of Victoria.

One important aspect of the dredger scheme mentioned only obliquely in the song was its financing. To "tot the public ledger" was really unnecessary since the Road and Harbor Act of 1862 had already

AN ACT

To authorize the Governor of Vancouver Island to borrow the sum of Forty Thousand Pounds on the security of the General Revenue of the said Colony.

WHEREAS, it is expedient to raise by Loan secured on the General Revenue of the said Colony, funds for the construction of Roads and other communications within the said Colony, and for the improvement of Victoria Harbour, and to make provisions for the redemption of such Loan.

And whereas, by the "Victoria Harbour Act, 1860," all monies and dues paid and levied in pursuance of "The Victoria and Esquimalt Harbour Dues Act, 1860," were directed to be paid into a separate account in the Treasury as a security for certain loans therein mentioned.

And whereas, since the passage of the said "Victoria Harbour Act, 1860," the loans effected by virtue of the said Act have been wholly paid off and redeemed.

Be it therefore enacted by His Excellency the Governor, on Her Majesty's behalf, by and with the consent of the Legislative Council and Assembly, as follows:

Repeal of the Victoria Harbour Act.

I. The "Victoria Harbour Act, 1860," is hereby repealed.

The Governor may issue Debentures to the amount of £40,000.

II. It shall be lawful for the Governor for the time being of the said Colony from time to time, or at any time hereafter, to cause to be made out and issued, Debentures secured upon the General Revenue of the said Colony, for such sum or sums of money not exceeding Forty Thousand Pounds (£40,000) Sterling in the whole, as may be required for the purpose of constructing roads and other communications within the interior of the said Colony, and for the purpose of improving Victoria Harbour.

III. All Debentures made out and issued under this Act shall bear interest at the rate of Six Pounds (£6) Sterling per

Nearly all the £40,000 was spent on the unsuccessful dredger scheme— and accounted for Vancouver Island's portion of the colonial debt at Confederation.

arranged for borrowed money. The public debt of $200,000, which the Vancouver Island colony incurred through this act, was carried first into the unified colony of British Columbia in 1866 and thence, as nearly the total Vancouver Island indebtedness, into Confederation in 1871. Had it not been for the dredger loan and its interest, Vancouver Island would have remained solvent. Perhaps by 1867 this debt had been merged in people's minds with the mainland's Cariboo Wagon Road debt; it belonged to the past and would be paid off by either Canada or the United States, whichever one British Columbia joined. In contrast to the mainland which had a good road, Vancouver Island had little to show for its debt. In 1865 the *Colonist* referred to the dredger as "The Elephant," a sobriquet also given to the Cariboo Road; like white elephants they impoverished their possessors.

How simple it must have seemed in the fall in 1861 to turn Victoria into a port to rival San Francisco! All that was needed was a dredger and a few months work. The idea of improving the harbor appeared as early as March, 1860, in a letter to the *British Colonist;* the price of a dredger according to the correspondent would be $1000. In August, 1861, the Victoria Harbor Commission gave Governor Douglas its opinion that a steam dredger and diving bell should be procured from the United Kingdom. But in September, when the Commission's chairman, Capt. G.H. Richards of H.M.S. *Plumper*, saw a dredger at work in San Francisco, he wrote the other commissioners that a suitable machine could be obtained in California for about $10,000. Victoria's harbor could begin its new life by the following spring with San Francisco passenger ships berthing in the Inner Harbor instead of at Esquimalt. The Harbor Commission, caught up by Richards' confidence and enthusiasm, passed a resolution that a California-built dredger be acquired immediately. Governor Douglas welcomed the resolution, and late in December tenders were called. The only recorded bid was for $33,000, over three times Richards' figure.

Financial aid eventually came through negotiations with the Colonial Office, which had a special interest in helping Victoria become a commercial port. Sometime before March, 1859, London had asked Douglas's view on Victoria's being declared a free port; Douglas replied convincingly that, as a free port like Hong Kong, Victoria would benefit the Imperial economy. As things were, Douglas contended, nearly all the goods consumed on Vancouver Island came through San Francisco where import and municipal duties added about 30% to their cost, or about $450,000 out of an annual $1,500,000 in purchases. If these goods were imported directly from England, they would be cheaper than in San Francisco; Victoria would become the favored Pacific port for flour, grain, and manufactured goods, selling to Puget Sound communities, to the Russians in Alaska, and to the Sandwich Islands. Douglas's last argument was that in the colony itself "values of all kinds of property, and especially of real estate, would be enhanced." Douglas, on the direction of London, declared Victoria a free port in January, 1860. The support the London government gave to Victoria's dredging plan fitted Imperial interest in the free port and simply allowed Vancouver Island to borrow money in London.

While Capt. Richards's proposal was stirring the colony to action on the dredger scheme, the Harbor Commission at Governor Douglas's request was preparing a comprehensive report on the state of the harbor with recommendations. The report, presented to the Governor in February, 1862, showed that Richards's dredging plan was but the first part of a task which was forecast to take six or seven years. This included removal of several rocks obstructing the harbor. The basic equipment required was a steam dredger, a tug, small scows or punts to carry away the dredged material, and a diving bell. The Commission found that dredging was needed just to maintain the depth of the harbor, which was daily receiving ashes and rubbish from ships in addition to material washed down the town's drains. The first constructive dredging was to widen the channel over the shoal spit or bar, which reached from Shoal Point across much of the harbor mouth, and to deepen and extend the berthing area to accommodate larger steamers. The bar had only eight feet of water at low tide and needed at least fifteen.

Financing was arranged by the Vancouver Island Assembly which passed legislation to enable the sale of bonds guaranteed, ironically, by the general revenue of the colony. Although the face value of the bonds was £40,000 or about $200,000 at 6% per annum interest, with discounts the money raised was less. The legislation stated the funds would be used for "constructing roads and other communications within the interior of [the] colony and for the purpose of improving Victoria Harbour." As it turned out the dredging by itself used the bulk of the funds.

To conserve money it was decided to assemble the dredger and the tug in Victoria. The two steam engines, the dredger's buckets and endless chain, and other materials were to be brought from England. Pemberton, Surveyor General of the colony and member of the Harbor Commission, was sent to the United Kingdom in April, 1863, to investigate dredger designs and arrange the purchase. Bucket dredgers were still making news in engineering journals in the 1860's. Vessels carrying all the machinery and materials arrived in Victoria via Cape Horn in July, 1864. Also aboard were two engineers hired on a six-year contract; their first job was to fit the engines and machinery into the hulls already under construction in Victoria and get them working.

The dredger anchored on the south shore of James Bay, an embarrassing reminder to occupants of the Legislative Buildings, the "Birdcages," seen behind. (A Notman photo taken from Indian Mission Hill, overlooking Songhees Reserve, 1871).

Public Archives of Canada

Capt. G.H. Richards's map of Victoria Harbor, 1861-1862, showing bar with low water of 1¼ fathoms extending from Shoal Point across the harbor mouth to West Bay.

1. Shoal Point
2. West Bay
3. The Bird Cages

There were many delays and hitches. Although the punts were finally ready in late December, the entire equipment was not tried out until March. On this trial the punt's unloading mechanism would not work, and still full it was towed back to the harbour mouth to be viewed by the disappointed Victorians. But greater problems could be traced to basic design. It soon became obvious that both the tug and the punts were too large. The tug drew too much water and couldn't serve the dredger at low tide. The dredger itself was patterned on machines used in such British estuaries as the Clyde with their gentle currents muddy bottoms. It did not adapt easily to the strong tidal currents on the outside of Shoal Point bar nor did its buckets work well when the mud and sand of the harbor bottom gave way to hard clay, gravel, coal and boulders, all of which were found in the first areas to be dredged. The bucket or ladder dredge had inherent shortcomings in tidal water; the angle of the ladder had to be continually adjusted and at low angles much of what was picked up fell out again. The buckets also churned a muddy bottom into a slurry which was largely water. It is no wonder that the machine got little done and broke down repeatedly.

Six years later, in 1871, after British Columbia had entered confederation, the man who had been in charge of the work was blamed for the fiasco. He was the superintendent of dredger operations, appointed to his position in February, 1865. In a report which dealt in part with the history of the harbor dredging, sent from Victoria to the Minister of Public Works in Ottawa, this man was said to have "failed entirely in working the machinery in a satisfactory manner." Further, the report said, "He was not an engineer, nor even a man of ordinary education

Modern view of Victoria Harbor   B.C. Government photo

and intelligence." These words, coming from the man who recommended his appointment, raise the question of where the incompetence lay. The writer, B.W. Pearse, had been Pemberton's assistant from the 1850's, and, after Pemberton's resignation in September, 1864, had become Acting Surveyor General. The report does not mention the design limitations of the dredger or the tug but does suggest the punts be replaced with smaller ones. The official stand seems to have made the superintendent the scapegoat.

The estimated costs of the dredger equipment and operation were first discussed in the Assembly in December, 1864. At that time Pearse was criticized in a *Colonist* editorial for being as much as 100% too low in his calculations. In 1871 Pearse confirmed his errors when he revealed to Ottawa the initial cost of the dredger, tug and punts had been $92,000 as opposed to the $47,500 in his estimates, dated January, 1865. Pearse may have been wiser by 1871 when he estimated the cost of four year's dredger operations at over $100,000. In June, 1865, when the Island's Legislative Assembly faced up to the real costs of continuing the harbor improvement, the majority supported a resolution that the program be suspended and that the superintendent and all his crew be paid off.

Although financial decisions marked the beginning and end of dredging during the colonial period, if the motivation and the incompetence of the key persons are put aside, the failure can be laid to the dredger design. The proposal of the songwriter was in part serious when he suggested the "dirty little dredger" be sent to dig in Mud Bay, where the deposits of the Serpentine and Nicomekl Rivers were ideal for its design. It would be many years before vertical action dredgers were developed to adequately meet the technical problems of Victoria's harbor.

After British Columbia joined Canada and the Department of Public Works in Ottawa was given the responsibility for harbor improvement, the dredging progressed intermittently. By 1880 the Shoal Point bar had been deepened three to four feet over a distance of 200 feet. By this time Victoria was urging maintenance dredging along the dockside and in the harbor's central basin where erosion from the unpaved streets, sewage and rubbish were building up. Since the odor of the shallow end of James Bay was becoming increasingly offensive and was regarded as a health hazard, Ottawa was asked to fill it in with material dredged from the nearby bottom. This would not be done until after the new legislative buildings were opened in 1899 and Victoria, desperately wanting its face improved, welcomed a C.P.R. tourist development which saw, in 1908, the Empress Hotel opened on the reclaimed land. The filling in and reclaiming had first been proposed in the Harbor Commission's report over forty years before.

Stanley G. Triggs

34

The Fraser River &
The Cariboo Gold Rushes

B.C. Provincial Archives

6

Far From Home

Where might-y wat-ers foam and boil And rush-ing tor-rents roar, In Fras-er Riv-er's north-ern soil Lies hid the gol-den ore. Far from home, Far from home On Fras-er Riv-er's shore We lab-our hard, so does our bard, To dig the gol-den ore.

1.
Where mighty waters foam and boil
And rushing torrents roar,
In Fraser River's northern soil
Lies hid the golden ore.
Chorus
Far from home, far from home
On Fraser River's shore
We labour hard, so does our bard,
To dig the golden ore.

2.
Far, far from home we miners roam,
We feel its joys no more.
These we have sold for yellow gold
On Fraser River's shore.

3.
In cabins rude, our daily food
Is quickly counted o'er.
Beans, bread, salt meat is all we eat—
And the cold earth is our floor.

4.
Lonely our lives—no mothers', wives',
Or sisters' love runs o'er
When home we come at set of sun
To greet us at the door.

5.
At night we smoke, then crack a joke,
Try cards 'til found a bore.
Our goodnight said, we go to bed
To dream of home once more.

6.
With luck at last, our hardships past,
We'll head for home once more,
And greet the sight with wild delight
Of California's shore.

7.
And once on shore, we never more
Will roam through all our lives:
A home we'll find, just to our mind,
And call our sweethearts wives.

Harper's New Monthly Magazine, Dec. 1860

*After the great rush of 1858 collapsed in the "Fraser Humbug," Californians
regained their hopes in the upper Fraser River creeks.*

A Rich Man's Goldrush

The handful of prospectors and miners who in 1860 and 1861 made the first notable gold discoveries in the Cariboo creeks were seasoned frontiersmen. By the summer of 1861, some 1500 men hearing of these findings had converged on the creeks. This first rush of miners came from the Thompson and lower Fraser Rivers, from the coast, and from elsewhere in the cordilleran region as far south as California. They brought with them years of experience in placer mining. Among them were packers and traders building trails and setting up stores.

The first high concentrations of coarse gold were found on bed rock which here and there lay exposed where the creeks had cut through deep glacial deposits. Although the miners could use sluice box and rocker on these already exposed areas, to get at the still-hidden gold they had to sink shafts and tunnel or "drift." For such enterprises miners joined together into companies. Their many hands were needed for digging and timbering, for making flumes, pumps, railcars and tracks all of wood. To join such a company the miner had to have capital. People who understood deep placer mining quickly recognized that Cariboo was a rich man's goldfield.

It was not news of this complex mining that brought the second wave of the gold rush in 1862 and 1863. All that was heard round the world was that gold could be readily picked off the bed rock with but little digging. The name "Cariboo" became a call to El Dorado, as had "California" in 1849 and "Australia" in 1851. Men of some means or those who could borrow set sail from the eastern United States, Canada, the United Kingdom, Europe and other corners of the world. These adventurers contrasted markedly with the hard-bitten miners already on the creeks. The newcomers generally had some formal education and gentility of manners and shared the hope of leaving the goldfields with enough wealth to give them a respected position in the growing middle class. Gold was not just a short cut to easy street but a way of gaining a foot on the social ladder of the new industrial society. Many of these would-be miners were unable to overcome the physical hardships of Cariboo life even if their money held out for a time. By 1865 when the gold takings were on the decline, they faced reality and made their way to the coast, broken in body and spirit.

In the years following the California gold rush of 1849 men listened eagerly for news of fresh strikes elsewhere in the western mountain or Cordilleran region of North America. In a number of places hopes were raised and then fell again. When news spread that gold from the Fraser River area had arrived at a mint in San Francisco, the mood was right for another rush. The gold to be minted had actually come to the Hudson's Bay Company from its Thompson River trading posts, but it became associated with the news late in 1857 that flakes and grains of gold had been found on a sand and gravel bar of the lower Fraser. During the summer and early fall of 1858 some 25,000 men reached the river, most coming aboard ship through San Francisco and disembarking at Victoria or on the shores of Puget Sound. Some came overland, drawing with them in their enthusiasm soldiers, sailors and loggers who simply left their posts or jobs to get what they dreamed would give them quick wealth. Many of the gold seekers were immediately discouraged, for they found the gold-bearing sand was in a surface layer of the river bars only three inches to two feet in depth. Further, the river water, at its highest level during the summer, covered the bars; there were too many men for what was exposed. It soon became clear that the source of the wealth found in the Hope-Yale vicinity lay undiscovered beyond the deadly Fraser Canyon, perhaps hundreds of miles away. Dubbing the rush the "Fraser River Humbug," most of the men left, many returning to California. As the water of the river receded, enough ground was revealed to sustain those who stayed, either with immediate rewards or with continuing hopes. Some nine thousand men remained through the 1858 winter with its long freezing spell, working the bars until the following summer's high water. By the summer of 1859 many had begun to find their way to the waters above the Canyon, but others stayed on the lower river at dry workings or waited for the water to fall again. "Far From Home" was dated "July, 1859" at Emory's Bar, located between Hope and Yale, B.C.

McCord Museum, Montreal

White gold-seekers left the bars of the lower Fraser when discoveries were made in Cariboo. In 1862 William G.R. Hind documented these Chinese miners at work between Hope and Yale.

Young Man From Canada

I'm a young man from Can-a-da, Some six feet in my shoes. I

left my home for Car-i-boo On the first ex-cit-ing news. In

New York Ci-ty I met a gent, In-tro-duced him-self to me; Said

I, "I come from Can-a-da, So you can't come o-ver me!" Said

I, "I come from Can-a-da, So you can't come o-ver me!"

1.
I'm a young man from Canada,
Some six feet in my shoes.
I left my home for Cariboo
On the first exciting news.
In New York City I met a gent,
Introduced himself to me;
Said I, "I come from Canada,
So you can't come over me!"

Chorus
Said I, "I come from Canada,
So you can't come over me!"

2.
I sailed on the crazy *Champion*
All in the steerage too,
I thought I'd got among the fiends
Or other horrid crew.
If you had only seen them feed!
It quite astonished me,
And I'd been years in Canada
In a lumberman's shanty.

3.
With seventy-five upon my back
I came the Douglas way,
And at an easy-going pace
Made thirty miles a day.
I landed here without a dime
In eighteen sixty-three,
But I'd been raised in Canada—
'Twas nothin' new to me.

4.
In best of home-spun I was clad
So I was warmly dressed;
The wool it grew near Montreal
At a place in Canada West.
On Williams Creek they called me green
And "Johnny-come-late-lee"—
Said I, "I come from Canada;
I ain't from the old country!"

5.
I started out my mining life
By chopping cord wood.
But I was born with axe in hand
So I could use it good;
My chum was from the state of Maine—
Somewhere near Tennessee—
But ah, I came from Canada
And he couldn't chop with me.

6.
In a short time I'd made a "raise"
And bought into a claim;
There they called me engineer
Or carman—'tis the same.
The drifters then did try it on
To boss it over me—
Said I, "I come from Canada,
And I'm on the *shoulder-ee.*"

7.
In two weeks I got a "div"
Which drove away all care—
I went over to the "Wake Up's"
And had a bully square—
I danced all night till broad daylight
And a gal smiled sweet on me.
Said I, "I come from Canada
And I'm on the marry-ee."

8.
Now all young men who are in love,
And sure I am there's some—
Don't count your chicks before they're hatched,
For they may never come.
O when I asked that gal to wed,
She only laughed at me:
"You may come from Canada,
But you can't come over me!"

This painting by W.S. Hutton in 1864 shows Cariboo adventurers setting out "the Douglas way," i.e. by Lake Harrison and Lillooet.

Representative of those of the second wave who remained in Cariboo is the anonymous author of the song "I'm a Young Man from Canada." He was willing to take the main chance but was not dismayed when it did not come through. The middle class label partly fits him, for he tells us how because of their table manners he felt apart from his fellows both in the Canada West lumber camps and in the steerage accommodation of the ship in which he sailed from New York. Although he says he was used to being without money, he did have just enough for his passage via Panama to the head of the navigation on the Fraser River, followed by an energetic two to three-week journey on foot to Cariboo. In this he exhibits a key middle class virtue, the ability to endure hardship for the promise of future rewards. Lastly, he would have had some formal education. Since he probably came from the environs of Hawkesbury, now in Ontario, he would have attended one of the schools which were well-established there even in the 1840's.

The key to this young Canadian's survival in Cariboo may be credited to his physique and his lumberjack skills, but it is surely more than this. The boastful pride of this six-footer dressed in his homespun woolens may amuse us, but his self-assurance, his naive individualism, his sense of humor and his pioneer roots in the lumbering-farming community on the Ottawa River would have together enabled him to make his way in many pioneering situations. It could be that his eagerness to marry meant that he saw his future in the far west. He may well have stayed on after the gold rush to become a British Columbian.

Instead of the gold pan, Cariboo miners had to sink shafts and drive horizontal tunnels or drifts. The slopes were denuded of trees used as mine timbers, etc., as well as fuel.

The text printed here comes to us from the late 1860's (see Appendix), but it was sung years after the decline of the Cariboo. *The Miner* of Nelson, B.C. for May 1, 1897, has a report by the "travelling correspondent" of London's *Daily Mail* describing life in the booming Rossland mining camp. Included is an account of "a grizzled old placer miner, one of the Cariboo Veterans—who sang a number of old mining songs with great effect." The writer included as a sample stanza five printed above. "Cord wood" appears as "board wood," perhaps indicating the English writer's unfamiliarity with the unit of measure "cord."

The Leisure Hour, *April, 1865*

Before the Cariboo Wagon Road was completed in 1865, miners used foot trails. This artist's impression accompanied an account of an 1862 journey "to Cariboo and back."

8

Old Faro

Faro players in California typical of the period. The "paper collar" finery of the banker and dealer contrasts with the miner's rags.

I'll sing you now a mourn-ful song All of a fine old man Who lived some years in Car-i-boo All by his sleight of han'.

Chorus:
Come back Far-o, Far-o dear Or I'll sing too-ral-la-day-o, Come back Far-o, Far-o dear Sing too-ral-la-de-ay.

1.
I'll sing you now a mournful song
All of a fine old man
Who lived some years in Cariboo
All by his sleight of han'.

Chorus
Come back Faro, Faro dear
Or I'll sing too-ral-la-day-o,
Come back Faro, Faro dear
Sing too-ral-la-de-ay.

2.
Although he lay in his bed all day
He was wide awake at night,
And when the luck was on his side
His face beam'd with delight.

3.
At times he'd grumble of hard luck
And say he'd ne'er a dollar;
Yet he lived a jolly lord
And wore a paper collar!

4.
Ah, many a time he found me grub
When I had ne'er a red—
Now I must work ten hours a day
Since good old Faro's dead.

5.
What e'er you were, old Faro, dear
I'll not defame the dead—
Your ghost might haunt me some cold night
And "freeze me out" in bed.

Final Chorus
Goodbye Faro, Faro dear,
May you strike it in White Pine,
Goodbye Faro, Faro dear
And may we strike it here!

Along Barkerville's raised board walks were saloons with adjoining gambling rooms until a magistrate in 1868 made a change. Shown here is Madame Bendixon's Hotel de France, noted for her hurdy-gurdy dancers. Picture is before the fire of September, 1868.

The professional gamblers with their faro and monte tables lived off the miners, and nothing effectively hampered their games in Barkerville until in 1868 a magistrate's order prohibited them from operating in any room attached to a public saloon. "Everything is now silent and dark where formerly, night after night, the tables were surrounded by anxious groups in pursuit of fortune," wrote the Cariboo *Sentinel* describing the changed scene. In 1864 James Anderson vented his dislike of the professional gambler in a verse letter in Scots dialect:

> There is a set o' men up here
> Wha never works thro' a' the year
> A kind o' serpents, crawlin' snakes,
> That fleece the miner o' his stakes...

In 1868 as some packed up and left, the writer of "Old Faro" made the same point but this time it takes on the satirical form of a mock lament. "Old Faro" in the song is ostensibly dead and is being buried in a white pine box, but what is actually happening is that public gaming being now defunct, "Old Faro" has gone south to the 1868 silver strike at White Pine in southeast Nevada.

"Paper collars" appear in "Old Faro" and "Bar Room Song" (another of Anderson's songs) as a symbol of gentility and vanity; such disposable collars were used by some British Navy officers as late as the 1950's.

From the title page of the first edition (1868) of the Barker-ville publication containing the words to "Bonnie Are the Hurdies, O!"

Bonnie Are The Hurdies, O!

1.
There's naught but care on ilka han',
On every hour that passes, O!
An' Sawney, man, we hae nae chance
To spark amang the lasses, O!

Chorus
Bonnie are the hurdies, O!
The German hurdy-gurdies, O!
The daftest hour that ere I spent,
Was dancin' wi' the hurdies, O!

2.
A warldly race that riches chase,
Yet a' gangs tapselteerie, O!
An' every hour we spend at e'en,
Is spent without a dearie, O!

3.
Last summer we had lassies here
Frae Germany—the hurdies, O!
And troth I wot, as I'm a Scot,
They were the bonnie hurdies, O!

4.
There was Kate and Mary, blithe and airy,
And dumpy little Lizzie, O!
And ane they ca'd the Kangaroo,
A strappin' rattlin' hizzy, O!

5.
They danced at night in dresses light,
Frae late until the early, O!
But oh! their hearts were hard as flint,
Which vexed the laddies sairly, O!

6.
The dollar was their only love,
And that they lo'ed fu' dearly, O!
They dinna care a flea for men,
Let them coort hooe'er sincerely, O!

7.
They left the creek wi' lots o' gold,
Danced frae oor lads sae clever, O!
My blessin's on their 'sour kraut' heads,
Gif they stay awa for ever, O!

In 1865 miners who could afford the price of a dance showed their prowess by swinging their partners like this.

Although the Barkerville saloons already had women entertainers, much excitement was caused in the summer of 1865 when there arrived from San Francisco an organized group of dancing partners, complete with musicians. To the rhythms made by two fiddlers who reportedly sang raucously so the music could be heard above the noise of the stomping feet, the girls danced with the miners for a dollar a dance. Starved of women's company and faced with the troupe's determination to deal in nothing but dance steps, the men developed a style of dancing that both surprised and exhausted their partners. The main point of this step, as described by those who were there, was for the man to lift his partner repeatedly as high as he could off the floor, at the same time swinging her feet aloft.

The girls had come originally from continental Europe; hence in the song "Bonnie Are the Hurdies, O!," the "German" hurdy-gurdy girls. What about "hurdy-gurdy?" Here is a three part guess. First, the fiddlers may have on occasion used the genuine hurdy-fiddle, a mechanical contrivance used at that time by street musicians; or perhaps the fiddling, under the circumstances, sounded just as if it were done on those crude instruments. Second, the overall effect of the dance may have been a "hurdy-gurdy," which in both English and Scottish dialect is "an uproar, a disorder." Last, and the song's chorus supports this, there seems to be a play on words, employing the Scots dialect "hurdies" which means "the buttocks." The girls were often referred to simply as "the hurdies." They were another kind of gold-digger, but the *Cariboo Sentinel* newspaper said they worked hard for their money, considering the style of dancing.

Photo of Mosquito Creek, Cariboo, about 1868. The scene of the song MARY, COME HOME would, of course, have been winter.

10

Mary, Come Home

Oh, Mar-y, dear Mar-y, come home with me now; The
sleigh from Mos-qui-to has come. You prom-ised to live in my
lit-tle board house As soon as the pap'r-ing was done. The
fire burns bright-ly in the sheet-ir-on stove And the bed is made up by the
wall. But it's lone-some, you know, these long win-ter nights With
no-one to love me at all.

1.
Oh, Mary, dear Mary, come home with me now;
The sleigh from Mosquito has come.
You promised to live in my little board house
As soon as the pap'ring was done.
The fire burns brightly in the sheet-iron stove
And the bed is made up by the wall.
But it's lonesome, you know, these long winter nights
With no one to love me at all.

2.
Oh, Mary, dear Mary, come home with me now;
Old George with his *kuitan* is here.   *horse*
You can, if you like, have your drink of old Tom,
But I'd rather you'd drink lager beer.
I've come all this way through the cold drifting snow,
And brought you a message from Yaco;
And these were the very last words that she said:
"Kloshe waw-waw delate mika chako."

     "I promise truly I'll come to you."

3.
Oh, Mary, dear Mary, come home with me now;
The time by the watch, love, is three.
The night it grows colder, and George with the sleigh
Down the road now is waiting for me.
She stopped at a stump on her way up the hill
And whispered for me not to follow;
But pressing my hand ere I left her, she said,
"Delate nika chako tomollo."   *"I'll definitely come tomorrow."*

As the European men pursued their conquest, settlement, and exploitation of North America, on the frontier men of every rank and occupation—map-makers, traders, trappers, sod-busters, ranchers, miners, loggers, fishermen—took Indian, Metis or half-breed women for their wives. Some of these unions were, as they may be anywhere, arrangements of convenience. In the fur trade, for example, such a marriage secured trade ties and familiarized the trader with the language and customs of his wife's tribe. In the formidable conditions of the frontier, especially in the western Canadian fur trade, such a marriage in the long run was a matter of survival. We regard the map-makers and the men who followed them as heroes, yet have not seen the extent to which their success depended on their women partners. One local historian of B.C.'s Peace River region claims that in these women, wedded without formal legal ties "after the custom of the country," is to be found the real heroism, for without them nothing could have been accomplished. Although occasionally a marriage brought enduring companionship and affection into the life of an otherwise lonely man, all these women brought to their marriages the skills of making moccasins and other clothing, of netting snowshoes, and of doing countless other practical tasks. Recent studies of the role of these women should lead to their being given their rightful place in our history.

Among the men in the Canadian West who profited by this kind of partnership were a number of famous explorers and fur traders. Such a marriage made possible the practical successes of David Thompson, acclaimed by historians as the greatest map-maker the world has known. His marriage to Charlotte Small, daughter of an Irish fur trader and his Cree wife, was marked by affection, mutual respect and loyalty. When Thompson left the fur trade, he took Charlotte with him to Lower Canada where they continued to raise their family. They lived together for the rest of their lives, sharing the penury that was often the final lot of the fur trader. But usually fur traders abandoned their "country" wives when they left the west, though often providing for their children. The Nor'Wester William Connolly, for example, repudiated Suzanne, his Cree wife of twenty years who had borne him six children. (Their daughter Amelia was the wife of Sir James Douglas.) Connolly remarried, but, after his death, the children of his first marriage claimed a share of the estate, the court ruled that the fur-trade marriage was indeed legal. The decree further demonstrated the equity a wife had in her husband's success.

In "Mary, Come Home" we see a lonely man hoping to make a home with an Indian woman. It's a rather wistful song because although he's built a house for her, she seems not to be ready to settle down with him. In the mining camps such women were in demand as prostitutes or as wives and enjoyed a certain amount of independence. But unfortunately many of them were from backgrounds where the social fabric had been torn by disease and alcoholism. Cut loose from the social forms of their own people, they had to make choices in order to survive, and such freedoms held many hazards. We don't know whether Mary succumbed to hard liquor, "old Tom," or settled down in the newly-papered board house to become one of our pioneers.

A very different attitude to Indian women is revealed in "Chinook Song," preserved for us on the end papers of the diary (1864-1867) of Arthur S. Farwell, later Surveyor-General for the province of British Columbia. Unlike "Mary, Come Home," "Chinook Song" is a white man's sexual fantasy of seduction promising the "tsee klootchman" (sweet woman) things she can't resist — clothing, flour, sugar, biscuits— in exchange for her favors. No newly-papered board house here—just a blanket on the ground. This song could well have been sung or recited at stag parties in such a place as Ben Griffin's hotel in Victoria in the 1860's.

Chinook Song

Tsee klootchman, fly with *nika*   *sweet woman   me*
  Leave behind thy light *canim*   *canoe*
And we will *hyak klatawa*   *swiftly go*
  And seek the forest dim.
For a while forget the *salt chuck*   *sea*
  Where the silv'ry salmon play—
We will take a *tenas moosum*   *little sleep* (i.e. make love)
  While the daylight fades away.

Oh! Be not *kwass* with *nika*   *shy   me*
  But thy *seeowist* turn on me   *face* or *eyes*
For thou canst not fail but *kumtux*   *know*
  That I *hiyu tickie* thee   *greatly love*
Then breathe the soft *nowitka*   *yes*
  Kloshe chako to my arms   *nicely come*
And in the forest lonely
  I'll *nanitch* all thy charms.   *see*

I will *potlatch hiyu icktas*   *give much clothing*
  Nika mahkook sapolil,   *I'll buy flour*
Of sugar and *lebiskwee*   *biscuits*
  Nika mamook thee thy fill   *I'll give*
With *passesse* spread beneath us   *blanket*
  We'll *kapswalla* on the ground,   *steal* (as in *k. moosum:* make illicit love)
Klonas you will *klap* a *tenas*   *perhaps   find (become with) child*
  While the dew is falling down.

No authorship of this macaronic is indicated in Farwell's diary. I have standardized the spelling of the Chinook Jargon, using Edward H. Thomas' *Chinook: A History and Dictionary of the Northwest Coast Trade Jargon,* Portland, Ore., 1935. For a description of the jargon, see the note for "Seattle Illahee", pp. 61-62.

11

The Skedaddler

I'm dead broke, I'm dead broke, so I've noth-ing to lose ; I've the wide world be-fore me to live where I choose. I'm at home in the wild woods wher-ev-er I be; Tho' dead broke, tho' dead broke, the Ske-dad-dler is free.

1.
I'm dead broke, I'm dead broke, so I've nothing to lose;
I've the wide world before me to live where I choose.
I'm at home in the wild woods whereever I be;
Tho' dead broke, tho' dead broke, the skedaddler is free.

2.
Tho' creditors curse me, I care not a straw;
I heed not old Begbie, I laugh at his law.
There is game in the mountains, the rivers yield fish,
And for gold I can prospect whereever I wish.

3.
Where I fancy a spot, I my blankets unfold
And remain for a time there to prospect for gold.
And ne'er as a debtor shall I go to quod
While my keep I can make with my gun and my rod.

4.
While I sit by my fire and my baccy I blow
I heed not the cold winds, the frost or the snow.
Tho' alone in the mountains, at least I am free,
Tho' the ground is my bed and my roof, a pine tree.

5.
When I think on the past, I can't see I'm in fault;
Tho' I worked like a horse, yet I ne'er made my salt.
When my prospects were blighted, they stopped all my "jaw,"
And tho' honest at heart, I'm nowhere an outlaw.

6.
Yet tho' cleaned out and fizzled, I do not despair;
There's a land far from this one—I soon shall be there.
And if Providence leaves me my hands and my health,
The skedaddler may yet win both honor and wealth.

"The Skedaddler" is escaping from Cariboo, leaving his debts behind. Fortunate to have his health, he is an outdoorsman and is sure he can shift for himself. Many men in British Columbia have tried to demonstrate complete self-reliance; this spirit has seen them through hardships but it has also exposed them unnecessarily to hazardous conditions. Despite his bravado, he may, as a California and Cariboo style prospector, have a shorter survival than he thinks. Another song of the period, "The Days of '49," depicts with stark humor the ends of many who continued to rely on the gold pan, or to burrow in near-barren ground.

The words "skedaddle" and "skedaddler" came into popular usage during the American Civil War (1861-5) meaning "to retreat or run away" and "one who runs away or leaves." Some of the Americans in Cariboo had already skedaddled from involvement in the Civil War. In this song the word is of course removed from the common military context.

The Decline of Cariboo

By 1865 the annual production of the Cariboo gold fields was on the decline. By then the gold-seekers either were working as share-owners in already producing mines, or were hangers-on, with their visions of wealth fast disappearing. These, the losers in the gold rush game, worked where they could for subsistence wages or schemed how to survive under the threat of near-starvation in a rigorous climate. Since the storekeepers had accumulated so many bad debts, credit for prospectors dried up. Records from the time speak of men giving others help in emergencies; but people became less generous as the number of destitute grew. Many men, willing to work hard with others and denied the opportunity, left the creeks in ill-health and in a state of bitter disappointment.

Author photo

Illustration from W. Champness', 1865 articles "To Cariboo and Back." The miner's condition is pictured before and after trying his fortune.

Towards Confederation

(Canadian *Illustrated News*, Sept. 9, 1876)

Uncle Aleck: Don't frown so, my dear, you'll have your railway by
and by.
Miss B. Columbia: I want it now. You promised I should have it, and if I
don't, I'll complain to Maw.

Dr. J.S. Helmcken and Cariboo's Dr. R.W.W. Carrall, shown at Niagara Falls in 1870 on their way to Confederation meetings in Ottawa.

12

Song of the "Dominion Boys" In British Columbia

Come, boys, let's sing a song! For the day it won't be long, When u-nit-ed to our count-ry we will be; Then the Map-le Leaf ent-wined And the Beav-er too, com-bined With Old Eng-land's flag shall float up-on the sea.

Chorus:

Tramp! tramp! tramp! the New Dom-in-ion Now is knock-ing at the door. So, good bye, dear Unc-le Sam, As we do not care a clam For your green-backs or your bun-kum an-y more.

1.
Come, boys, let's sing a song!
For the day it won't be long
When united to our country we will be,
Then the Maple Leaf entwined
And the Beaver too, combined
With Old England's flag shall float upon the sea.
Chorus
Tramp! Tramp! Tramp! the New Dominion
Now is knocking at the door.
So, goodbye, dear Uncle Sam,
As we do not care a clam
For your greenbacks or your bunkum any more.

2.
With your *Alabama* claims
And your other little games,
You thought "Old John" would gladly let us go;
And although Bright may be your friend,
That's a game that has an end,
When you trod upon the British Lion's toe.

3.
Then, boys, fill a bowl
And let each jolly soul
Labor as he never dared to do before.
And here's to thee, Sir John,
Whom we go our pile upon
And the Conjuration knocking at the door.

The colony of British Columbia became Canada's sixth province on July 20, 1871. But the event came about only after five years of posturing and debate among the several groups in the colony who had a stake in its future. By 1866 the height of the gold rush had passed and the population was decreasing. The colony was on the verge of bankruptcy, oppressed by an enormous and increasing debt. Everybody agreed that something had to be done. Where did the future of British Columbia lie? With Great Britain, the heart of Empire, providing colonial government, financial support and military protection? With the new Dominion of Canada? Or with the United States, aggressively looking for new territories to annex?

Cariboo, unlike Vancouver Island, was solidly in favor of joining Canada. "Cheer, Boys, Cheer for the Dominion Nation" (1868) and "Song of the 'Dominion Boys' in British Columbia" (1869) express the wholehearted commitment of the people of Cariboo to Confederation. The first of these uses the form of a contemporary English song on an emigration theme:

Cheer, boys, cheer! There's wealth for honest labour.
Cheer, boys, cheer for the new and happy land.

The second, an adaptation of an American Civil War song, comes from the "Dominion Boys" at Barkerville; these boosters of Confederation actually raised the flag described in the first stanza. The song welcomes Canada's overtures that the colony take advantage of Section 143 of the British North America Act (1867) which provided for the entry of other British territories to Confederation.

Printed in the *Cariboo Sentinel*, they were propaganda songs with more than local importance, telling Victoria, Ottawa, London, and Washington of a popular movement demanding immediate union with Canada. The issue of responsible government and other terms of union could be settled later. The general belief in Cariboo in the necessity of Confederation was the result of the geography and economic prospects of the region. Now that the gold rush was over, a new kind of mining community was struggling for a footing, and it would succeed only if transportation costs could be greatly reduced. Its staple product would still be placer gold, but the metal would be recovered with pumps and hydraulics. Hard rock mining would follow. But capital was needed and would only be forthcoming if Cariboo could be connected to the eastern economy, opening up trade and migration.

Since Great Britain would not impose an unpopular solution on the colony, the Confederationists, like the other interest groups, strove to

cont. P. 56

13

Cheer, Boys, Cheer,
For The Dominion Nation

the Con-fed-er-a-tion; The fair-est the free-est land un-der the sun.

Chorus
Cheer, boys, cheer, for the Dominion Nation,
Glorious the race that's before her to run;
Cheer, boys, cheer, for the Confederation;
The fairest, the free-est land under the sun.

1.
Cheer, boys, cheer, for the Dominion Nation,
Glorious the race that's before her to run;
Cheer, boys, cheer, for the Confederation;
The fairest, the free-est land under the sun.
For Britain hath said that the land is your own,
Then take and possess it from shore unto shore;
On the west lay your lines by Pacific's white foam,
On the east where Atlantic waves sullenly roar.

2.
And rich is the heritage, worthy the giver,
Her children in millions can here find a home,
In the forests and valleys, by lake and by river,
And on the plains where the herds of the bison now roam.
Then cheer, loudly, cheer, let no thought of care smother
Your bright bounding joy, or your fullness of glee;
To the south stretch your hands, grasp that of a brother,
From one common race sprung the sons of the free.

3.
And deep breathe the prayer, may no after strife sever
The Dominion from Albion, the brave and the free;
Long live our Queen! Rule Britannia for ever!
Dear land of our sires, proud Queen of the sea.
Then cheer, boys, cheer, for the Dominion Nation,
Glorious the race that's before her to run;
Cheer, boys, cheer for the Confederation,
The fairest, the free-est land under the sun.

demonstrate they had overwhelming support. In May, 1868, the call had gone out from Victoria to other centers in the colony to form branches of the newly-created Confederation League. What better way to do this in Cariboo than to call a meeting in Barkerville on the first anniversary of the creation of the Dominion of Canada? July 1 that year was celebrated in Barkerville with races and prizes, a minstrel show at the Theatre Royal, a grand ball and a brilliant display of fireworks. But first came the speeches and resolutions. The need for forming a branch of the Confederation League was urged on the assembled crowd at an open-air meeting in front of Scott and Lipsett's saloon. A key figure in the political proceedings was Dr. Robert W.W. Carrall, who moved the main resolution. It censured the government of British Columbia for opposing Confederation quite against "the declared wishes of the people of the colony." In 1869 a similar rally for Confederation was part of the Dominion Day festivities. That was the year the "Dominion Boys" flew their maple leaf and beaver ensign from a pole 115 feet high, far above all the other flags.

Dr. Carrall kept Prime Minister John A. Macdonald abreast of developments in the west. Early in 1869 Macdonald wrote him, exhorting him to "keep the Union fire alight until it burns over the whole Colony." Whatever the heat of Carrall's "Union fire," it could not ignite Victoria's officialdom, headed by Governor Seymour. Macdonald had to write Canada's Governor General: "It is quite clear that no time should be lost by [the Colonial Secretary in London] in putting the screws on at Vancouver Island and the first thing to be done will be to recall Governor Seymour."

On the question of Confederation, Governor Frederick Seymour was dragging his heels, obviously on the side of a small group of colonial officials and active or retired Hudson's Bay Company men; they were for the status quo and hoped Great Britain would see the colony through hard times. The officials wanted to protect their careers and pensions; the Bay men, the company's privileges. One influential leader with Hudson's Bay sympathies, Dr. J.S. Helmcken, associated himself with this group but despaired of getting help from Britain. Until 1870 he was strongly opposed to union with Canada and entertained the idea of joining the United States as the most practical answer to the colony's problem. The Confederationists, however, believed the the best course lay in joining the eastern provinces from which many of them had come. Their Confederation League, led by Amor de Cosmos, polarized the pro-union feeling on Vancouver Island and the mainland, and at the Yale Convention (Sept., 1868) drew up proposals for terms of union.

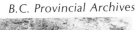

B.C. Provincial Archives

These miners in a drift mine on Lightning Creek about 1900, are working in exactly the same way as their predecessors some thirty years earlier. The benefits of Confederation dreamed of by the miners of the late 1860's did not materialize for many.

Yet another group—mainly merchants and traders in Victoria who had come from the United States—wanted that country to take the colony under its wing, to assume the debt and pour in money for expansion. London was investing nothing; Washington, however, was ready to invest heavily in western North America, and American railroad builders were talking seriously of a second trans-continental line reaching into the northwest. The Annexationists petitioned the President of the United States (Nov., 1869). Indeed, they could be assured that their petition would not fall on deaf ears, for proposals to purchase and annex British Columbia were much discussed in the United States. One such proposal, mentioned in "Song of the Dominion Boys'," was to make British Columbia part of the deal in the settlement of the *Alabama* claims.

During the American Civil War, Great Britain officially claimed

In the late 1860's, the main forces determining British Columbia's future would, in fact, cause it to join Canada, despite rumored dealings of annexationists to have it made over to the United States as part compensation for damage done during the American Civil War by the southern ship Alabama, *built and armed by the British. Shown in this* Harper's Weekly *cartoon are Jonathan Laird, M.P., and Reverdy Johnson, U.S. Minister to Britain. The irony in their meeting arises from the fact that the Alabama was laid in Laird's shipyard, which his sons took over on his entering politics in 1861.*

neutrality. It recognized the government of the Southern Confederacy and continued to trade with the South, for cotton was much in demand in the Lancashire mills and Confederate agents were purchasing arms in England. The North set up a shipping blockade, but British business interests conspired to aid the South. With apparent complicity of the British government, they built several "merchant" ships for the South and armed them. These "British pirates," the most notorious of which was the *Alabama*, either sank Northern shipping or drove it from the seas for some two years. The United States laid claims for reparation against the British government for not keeping its neutrality and in 1871 was awarded, by the Treaty of Washington, damages of $15,000,000. Recurrently from 1867, the idea that British Columbia might be taken in part payment was discussed by Americans. This was the time for such deals; had not Alaska been purchased from the Russians in 1867?

Indirect support for annexation came also from Great Britain, weary of the burden of Empire. Many Britons, wanting to get rid of the colonies, found in the ideas of John Bright a happy solution to the North American colonial issue. This radical British reformer envisaged the whole continent under the American flag, fulfilling in Bright's words the promise of "freedom everywhere, equality everywhere, law everywhere, peace everywhere." From his side of the Atlantic, Bright held great hopes for the United States, which did not have Britain's hereditary class priviliges and where the franchise was much broader than in England.

In "Song of the 'Dominion Boys'," the second stanza and half the chorus is directed against the Annexationists. Although the song was published in preparation for Barkerville's 1869 Dominion Day festivities, its author(s) knew it would reach the ears of the very vocal but not large pro-American faction in Victoria. It treats them as straw men, as it calls with uncritical zeal for immediate union with Canada. For good measure "Dominion Boys" adds a taunting reference to the "greenbacks," the paper money issued by the North during the Civil War, which had depreciated drastically in value.

Fortuitously, Governor Seymour died of illness before he could be recalled, and his successor was instructed by the Colonial Office to do everything he could to bring about union with Canada. In the spring of 1870, Dr. Carrall, Dr. Helmcken (finally won over to Confederation) and Joseph W. Trutch travelled to Ottawa to discuss the terms of union. They came back with more than the Cariboo populace ever hoped for: the $1,300,000 debt to be taken over by Ottawa, a substantial annual per capita grant, superannuation for the worried civil servants, and, almost beyond belief, a railway to be completed in ten years. The future of British Columbia now seemed assured, and the people of Cariboo were jubilant. Nevertheless, union with Canada came as a bit of an anticlimax in Barkerville. They had, after all, been celebrating Dominion Day ever since its first anniversary in 1868.

Pioneering,
Sod~Busting & Settling In

14

Seattle in late 1870's

Seattle Illahee (I)

1. There'll be mow-itch And klootch-man by the way When we 'rive at Se-at-tle Il-la-hee.

Chorus:
Row, boys, row! Let's trav-el To the place they call Se-at-tle, Se- at-tle Il-la-hee!

2. There'll be hi-yu clams And klootch - man by the way
Hi-yu ten-as moos-um Till day-light fades a- way.

3. Kwone-sum kwone-sum cool-ey Ko-pa ni-ka il-la - hee Ku- na-
mokst kaps-wal-la moos-um as the day-light fades a- way.

var. a)-ad lib.
at-tle That's the place to have a spree! Se - at-tle Il-la-hee!

60

1.
There'll be *mowitch*   *venison*
And *klootchman* by the way   *woman*
When we 'rive at Seattle *Illahee*   *place*

Chorus
Row, boys, row! Let's travel
To the place they call Seattle
(That's the place to have a spree!) AD LIB
Seattle Illahee

2.
There'll be *hiyu* clams   *plenty*
And klootchman by the way
Hiyu *tenas moosum*   *'little sleep'*
Till daylight fades away.

3.
Kwonesum kwonesum cooley   *always running (or going)*
Kopa nika illahee   *at my living place*
Kunamokst kapswalla moosum   *together steal*
As the daylight fades away.

"Seattle Illahee" appears to be the oldest song yet found orally in the Pacific Northwest. "Seattle Illahee (I)" was sung at Campbell River on Vancouver Island. A fragment of a variant with almost the same words and verse form but with a different tune and no chorus was found in the south Okanagan of British Columbia in 1961. Since the two versions have a similar pattern of words taken from the Chinook jargon, the song may even go back to the first half of the nineteenth century when Fort Vancouver (now Vancouver, Wash.) was the center of Hudson's Bay Company trade. It may have then generated both inland and coastal versions. Another coastal song "Seattle Illahee (II)" shares the chorus and the interest in sex of "Seattle Illahee (I)."

The Chinook jargon or trade language in some form is thought to predate the arrival of the companies of fur traders. It takes most of its vocabulary from the proper Chinook language spoken by the Indian people at the mouth of the Columbia River, but has in addition words from other coast languages as far north as the Nootkan (Vancouver Island). Through the influence of the fur trade, and especially in the early 1800's of those fur traders and trappers who married and lived among the Indian people, the language grew to include French and English derivatives. Words of the old jargon, not uncommon in English vernacular here today, are "chuck" (water), "salt chuck" (sea), and "skookum" (strong).

In trying to date the coastal songs, a clue may be found in the Chinook term "Seattle illahee." In the jargon, "Seattle Illahee" means "the place Seattle," in the same way that "Boston Illahee" means the U.S.A. and "King Chauch (George) Illahee," England; it may be that this literal meaning is all that is implied. However, in Seattle in the early 1860's, "illahee" came to have a more specific meaning. At that time the first bawdy house in the northwest was opened with the name "Illahee," under the entrepreneurship of a Mr. John Pennell who arrived from San Francisco. Locally, the place came to be known as "Down on the Sawdust" or "The Madhouse," but its fame spread throughout the whole Puget Sound area, where there was an increasing number of mateless males. According to some historians, it was the opening of "Illahee" that put Seattle, rather than any other of several neighboring communities, in the mainstream of northwest trade. A chronicler of the period had said of the "Illahee" that it "had a powerful imaginative effect on the whole male population of the Puget Sound Country, and old timers still relate fabulous legends from those happy days."

62

Penticton Museum

Harry Robb's mill

15

My Name 'Tis Vernon Fetterly

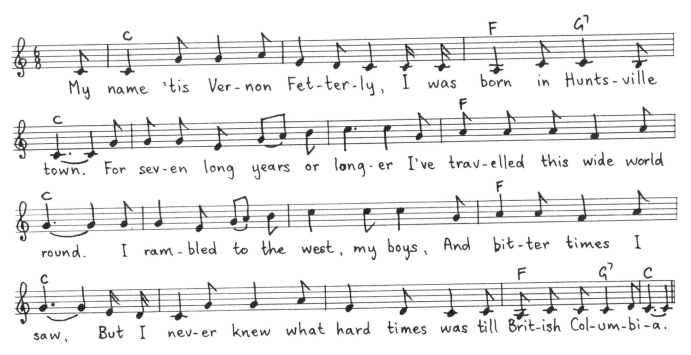

My name 'tis Ver-non Fet-ter-ly, I was born in Hunts-ville town. For sev-en long years or long-er I've trav-elled this wide world round. I ram-bled to the west, my boys, And bit-ter times I saw, But I nev-er knew what hard times was till Brit-ish Col-um-bi-a.

1.
My name 'tis Vernon Fetterly,
I was born in Huntsville town.
For seven long years or longer
I've traveled this wide world round.
I rambled to the west, my boys,
And bitter times I saw,
But I never knew what hard times was
Till British Columbia.

2.
In eighteen hundred and sixty-two
In the merry month of June
I landed in British Columbia
On a Saturday afternoon.
Up stepped a long-legged skeleton
His name was Harry Robb.
He invited me to his hotel
The best in British Columbia.

3.
I rose from bed next morning
To look around the place.
Before I wandered very far
Harry stared me in the face,
Said he'd give me board and lodging
If in his mill I'd saw
He said I'd ne'er regret the day
I hit British Columbia.

4.
Well, I took the job with Harry Robb—
I'll ne'er forget his frame,
He stood six-foot-seven in his shoes
As lean as any crane;
His hair hung down in rat tails,
He had a lantern jaw.
A specimen of the men you see
In British Columbia.

5.
He fed me on corn dodgers
Just as hard as any rock,
Till my teeth began to loosen
And my knees began to knock.
You should have seen the look of me,
I could hide behind a straw
You bet I regretted the day I came
To British Columbia.

6.
I've little flesh upon my bones,
Just enough to shiver.
Before the ice has froze me in,
I'm going down the river.
If ever I see your land again
I'll hand to you my paw,
But it will be through a telescope
That I see British Columbia.

63

When Vernon Fetterly recorded this song in August, 1961, he was still ranching near Okanagan Falls. Although he was then over seventy years of age, he rode that summer in the round-up. He was a big heavily-built man who, before turning to ranching many years earlier, had been a blacksmith in Penticton. Prior to that he had worked at logging and sawmill jobs, using the knowledge and skills brought with him from the woods of Ontario, where he had been a young lumberjack. Vernon Fetterly came into the southern Okanagan region of British Columbia about 1907 from Huntsville, Ontario, which is today still a thriving lumbering community.

The song is a bit of a bunkhouse or boarding-house joke perpetrated by a spirited young man on his employer. The humor is based in part on his standards of excellence, especially in regard to the food provided in the "best" hotel in British Columbia. Also a matter of fun is the outlandish appearance of the employer, who supplies room and questionable board as an inducement to work for him. The young migrant placed the date of the occurrence in 1862, around the time the first gold-seekers came into the region, perhaps to underline that the song was tongue-in-cheek in case his satire was taken too seriously. Harry Robb did run a sawmill in the Penticton area. Any of Vernon Fetterly's audience who had travelled the country as he had or had come from the lumbering shanties would have known the song on which his was based. In the original the traveler satirized the conditions in the State of Arkansas (see Appendix). In any case, the young Fetterly did not leave this region but stayed and raised a family here.

Vernon Fetterly had very definite musical taste and spoke of such songs as "Jimmy Whalen," "The Jam on Gary's Rocks" and the "Wreck of the Asia" as his kind of music. Although he was not known as a singer, like most people who work alone he probably occasionally sang as he rode the range—and recalled with a chuckle the time he made the song on Harry Robb. He certainly chuckled when he recorded it.

Vernon Fetterly's blacksmith shop is shown at right in this photo of riders and a pack train at Penticton. The rider with the pack animals is Babe Kruger, reputed to have known and sung many old songs.

16

The Old Go-Hungry Hash House

1.
The flapjacks they were leather—
They'd stand up in any weather—
You could even sew them on as soles for shoes.
The syrup it was paint,
If you smelled it you would faint,
And the prunes were dated "eighteen forty-nine."

Chorus
Then we open up the gates—
Oh, we all rush in on roller skates
In the old go-hungry hash house where I board!

2.
The sausages were sawdust—
It'd make you smile your broadest
To hear them claim that they were made of pork!
And we never got enough
Of that beef that was so tough—
You couldn't stick the gravy with a fork!

3.
The biscuits, they were wooden,
And we had some cast-iron pudding;
You couldn't break the pie-crust with a club.
And if you weren't a lover
Of the landlady's daughter,
Oh, you'd never get a decent plate of grub!

B.C. Archives

*Unmarried men at the turn of the century in British Columbia might "board"
with an established family, like the Herridges of Nakusp (1893).*

Vancouver Public Library

...or live in a residential hotel like the one shown here at Ferguson, c. 1900.

Around 1900 the population of the growing towns and cities of British Columbia had often more than twice as many males as females. The large number of unmarried men faced the problem of finding some sort of accommodation. Depending on income, class orientation and steadiness of employment, they found different solutions. Some, either alone or in pairs, "batched" in shacks of tents or in rooming houses. Some would get meal tickets on a weekly or monthly basis at a restaurant. Others found home comfort boarding with established families. Then there were the boarding houses where, in addition to sleeping facilities, food, heat, light, and often a common sitting room, there would be some regular companionship at least at meal times. That we have boarding house songs is testimony that the experience was common and further, that boarding-house fare was not always good. The conditions which elicited these wry verses probably resulted from a combination of inadequate transportation and refrigeration and the desire of boarding-house keepers to cut costs by buying cheaper grades of food.

The chorus of "The Old Go-Hungry Hash House" springs from an indoor roller-skating craze which swept the American continent in the 1880's. In Vancouver Hart's Opera House doubled for a while in the late 1880's as a roller rink, a far cry from the "roller-skating palaces" the big cities in the east vaunted.

17

Klondike!

Oh, come to the place where they struck it rich, Come where the treas-ure lies hid! Where your hat full of mud is a five-pound note And a clod on your heel is a quid! Klon-dike! Klon-dike! lab-el your lug-gage for Klon-dike. Oh, there ain't no luck in the town to-day; There ain't no work down Mood-y-ville way. So pack up your traps and be off, I say, Off and a-way to the Klon-dike!

Chorus
Klondike! Klondike!
Label your luggage for Klondike.
Oh, there ain't no luck in the town today;
There ain't no work down Moodyville way.
So pack up your traps and be off, I say,
Off and away to the Klondike!

1.
Oh, come to the place where they struck it rich,
Come where the treasure lies hid!
Where your hat full of mud is a five-pound note
And a clod on your heel is a quid!

2.
Oh, they scratches the earth and it tumbles out,
More than your hands can hold;
For the hills above and the plains beneath
Are crackin' and bustin' with gold!

The gold rush in the Yukon Territory—which is the real northwest of Canada—began when in the summer of 1896 news spread down the coast of a gold find on a tributary of the Klondike River. Within a year the territory's new name "Klondike" was luring men from all corners of the earth. At its peak, the "Trail of '98" passed through Seattle, Vancouver and other northwest ports to bring an end to the slump which for five years had gripped the economies of both Washington State and British Columbia. During this depression, which hit the continent's business in 1893, many British Columbia companies in the primary industries of lumbering, fishing and mining had been consolidated and came under the control of British, eastern Canadian and American capital. The running tide of the gold rush brought along with the transients more immigrants. Merchants became "Klondike Outfitters." Real estate values soared, and the Pacific Northwest was booming again. In the next decade Vancouver's population multiplied five times to 100,000 and Seattle's reached 240,000.

In the song "Klondike!" an unemployed worker dreams of the gold fields in contrast to the bleak scene in the sawmill community of Moodyville, now part of the foreshore of the city of North Vancouver.

Outfitters on Cordova Street, Vancouver, use a pack mule train to promote their Klondike supplies.

Vancouver City Archives

The call of the Klondike did not sound so strong to the employed workers; those in the hard rock mines, especially members of the Western Federation of Miners, stuck to their jobs and ideals, and through legislation in 1899 won the eight-hour day for underground workers. The law appears to be the first of its kind to take effect in North America and demonstrated the vigor of radical political persuasion in British Columbia at the time.

Vancouver City Archives

"...there ain't no work down Moodyville way." *Moodyville sawmill 1898.*

Public Archives of Canada

Steamer Islander *starting for Goldfields, Klondike, from Victoria, B.C., 1897.*

Hip-Hip-Hoorah
For My Native Canada

Hip - hip - hoor - ah for my nat - ive Can - a - da, The
Queen of the Sum - mer and the Lad - y of the Snow ! Oh, the
land I love the best Is the reg - ion in the west Where the
wild flow - ers blos - som And the moun - tain map - les grow.
Green are the hills where the riv - ers and the rills Join the
song of the spring - time as they jour - ney to the sea. Where the
orch - ard trees are ripe And the mead - ows blos - som bright And the

blue bird is call-ing to the rob-ins in the tree.

1.
Hip-hip-hoorah for my native Canada,
The Queen of the Summer and the Lady of the Snow!
Oh, the land I love the best
Is the region in the west
Where the wild flowers blossom
And the mountain maples grow.

2.
Green are the hills where the rivers and the rills
Join the song of the springtime as they journey to the sea.
Where the orchard trees are ripe
And the meadows blossom bright,
And the blue bird is calling
To the robins in the tree.

3.
Hip-hip-hoorah for my native Canada,
The Queen of the Summer and the Lady of the Snow!
Oh, the land I love the best
Is the region in the west
Where the wild flowers blossom
And the mountain maples grow.

Margaret Lang Hastings Collection

*Against a background of wild roses, students aged 6-16 of Mud Bay School
pose with their teacher, Mr. F.W. Templer, about 1903.*

Official anthems may be imposed in some nations, but Canada's history, bi-cultural heritage and regionalism have made our politicians wary of taking such a step and have frustrated the attempts of others to produce a generally accepted song to symbolize national unity. In 1964 the federal government of the day barely managed to have our maple leaf flag proclaimed as the official flag of Canada; the issue of "O Canada," with its original French words and an English translation, was diverted to a Royal Commission. Up to that time nearly twenty different sets of words, all of them adaptations rather than translations, had been published. The Commission's suggestions met with enough objections that still one hundred ten years after the British North America Act created Canada, the country is without an official anthem.

What is the significance of a national song, and what does it mean if a country does not have one? In the year 1977 when the new Confederation Debate was underway, it was difficult not to see the lack of a song as symptomatic of something in the Canadian union; whether this is a strength, a weakness, or irrelevant, seems to be a peculiarly Canadian conundrum.

The only national songs I have encountered in my fifty years as pupil and teacher in British Columbia public schools are the first stanza of "God Save the King (or Queen)" and the initial stanza of "O Canada" from Weir's 1908 adaptation. I have been told that "The Maple Leaf Forever" was sung in some schools as late as the 1940's. Today "God Save the Queen" is heard less and less. By about 1960 enough of the movie-going public in Vancouver were either rushing out of the theatre at the end of the last show before the concluding anthem, or sitting disrespectfully through it, that the cinemas discontinued a custom which dated back before World War I. Now such attitudes are without doubt reflected in the schools. Only "O Canada" remains, but its status is unofficial.

In 1902 another national song was sung by the pupils at the pioneer Mud Bay School. The one-room school was situated a few yards from the Mud Bay Church on the flats between the Serpentine and Nicomekl Rivers some 1½ miles upstream from Mud Bay, a northeast section of Boundary Bay. From 1902 to 1904 a Mr. F.W. Templer was the teacher of some 37 boys and girls ranging in age from 6 to 16. The average attendance was 19. Most of the parents were prosperous farmers settled on the rich surrounding lands. In the inspector's view the low attendance and the fact that no student had been prepared for High School for a number of years was owing to "a lack of interest" on their part. Mr. Templer, shown with some of the 1902-03 class, opened and closed the day with a song. The morning song, "Hip-Hip-Hoorah for my Native Canada," was perhaps an attempt to awaken and to stimulate in his pupils a sense of Canadian identity. It was remembered fondly over seventy years later by Vern Seidelman, the ten-year-old with bare feet at the left of the photograph. The source of the song is as yet unknown.

19

Pembina River Homestead

Near the Pem - bin - a Riv- er the grass - es grow high, And
if you take a home - stead pre - pare for to die. In the
land of Al - ber - ta, the land of the King, Horseflies and mos - quit - oes, much sor - row they bring.

1.
Near the Pembina River the grasses grow high,
And if you take a homestead prepare for to die.
In the land of Alberta, the land of the King,
Horseflies and mosquitos, much sorrow they bring.

2.
You must clear thirty acres to satisfy man;
And if you can't get thirty, then get what you can.
And after you've got it, oh, what will you grow?
A few rutabagas if it ain't too much snow.

3.
You go out to grub willows, you'll find it some job
For there's always plenty around your back yard.
You get mighty hungry while rolling the logs
And living alone with the coyotes and dogs.

5.
Your wife, she's half naked; your children, the same.
Oh, how it hurts you to hear them complain!
And they surely will ask you, "Do you intend to remain
And starve us to death on this government claim?"

6.
Now God will forgive me of this one rash act;
I'll take no more homesteads and this is a fact.
For the weather's so long I can hardly remain,
And I'm starving to death on this government claim.

Only three songs springing directly from homesteading experiences have, to my knowledge, been found in British Columbia, and all of them were made by discouraged Alberta homesteaders. The songs document a pattern of migration shared by many who came to this province after trying their fortunes elsewhere on the continent. For them, British Columbia was the last frontier—or perhaps the last chance.

Bill "Bud" Baldwin's song, "The Alberta Homesteader," was recorded in Surrey, B.C. in 1964 and can be seen in Edith Fowke's *More Folk Songs of Canada* (Waterloo, 1967, pp. 112-3). "The Pembina River Homestead" was recorded from the singing of J.C. Akers in 1973. He had come to Canada from Texas in 1912 and had taken up a homestead near the Pembina River west of Edmonton. Both songs complain of the climate and the prospect of starvation. Neither man faced these trials entirely alone. Although Bud Baldwin was a bachelor at the time, he had come from Ontario with a partner. Jim Akers had with him his wife and young family, on whom the privations of homestead life were particularly hard. That both men moved on to British Columbia indicates that they judged their homesteading prospects as poor. The songs document their feelings and some of their reasons for leaving.

Homesteading on the Canadian prairies began soon after Canada's first Land Act in 1872 provided for that mode of settlement. A Dominion survey of the land proposed for agricultural use divided the prairies into townships, which were six-mile squares comprising thirty-six sections or square mile areas. In each township, sixteen and one-quarter sections were designed for homesteaders. Nearly an equal amount was reserved for the railroad company which would open up

A homesteading family.

the region. The remainder were for the Hudson's Bay Company or were marked "school lands." Some of the surveyed lands, especially in the periphery towards the Rocky Mountains, were poor homestead sites. In this regard the land along the Pembina River serves as an example. The hundred-and-fifty-mile stretch from the Pembina's junction with the Athabasca had fairly good soil, but for a distance above that the land was marginal for farming. When cleared, some of it produced fodder crops for livestock, such as pigs and cattle. By the time of Jim Aker's arrival, the better land had been claimed. The Dominion survey included lands that were never homesteaded and others that were entered more than once and abandoned in disappointment.

"Pembina River Homestead" tells the essentials of Jim Akers's homesteading experience. That he hoped to gain title to the land in one year is indicated by his goal of clearing thirty acres of the one-hundred-sixty acres of his quarter section. Thirty acres appears in the Dominion Land Act, but they had to be cleared in a year. To get title to the land after such a short residence, he was also required to construct a habitable dwelling and, finally, to pay the Dominion government its assessed value of the land.

Under the homesteading provisions of the Dominion Land Act, there were two other ways of getting ownership of the land. The usual method was to live on the land for at least six months a year for three years, cultivating it each year. In the other six months the homesteader could work for necessary funds, usually on a railroad construction or for a more established farmer. Although the Act did not specify a minimum acreage to be cleared, Jim Aker's song likely reported a general view on the amount:

> You must clear thirty acres to satisfy man,
> And if you can't get thirty, then get what you can.

The third way was for the homesteader to fulfill the three-year residency requirement, have twenty head of cattle, and erect stables and outhouses for them.

Fortunately, in some cases cash might come with the clearing. If there were trees of the right size, they could be sold for telegraph poles or cut into railroad ties, both in great demand. Smaller trees, like the willows mentioned in the song, were made into slender poles and sold for prairie fencing. Each dollar, in these circumstances, would be saved to pay the fee for the land; and, if the prospects of the homestead looked poor, the money would pay for moving on. In either case there was nothing to spare for clothing and very little for food.

Once the homesteader gained title to the land, he could dispose of it as he wished. Most stayed, especially if their farms promised them a livelihood in return for their labors. Some homesteaders sold their land, receiving in their price the value of their improvements and of the title. This money was the key to a better farm or to other opportunities. A few acquired homesteads as speculations, gambling on the route of a railroad or the location of a town. But Jim Akers and his wife with two small children arrived in Alberta too late to produce a viable homestead. They moved to British Columbia but not to homestead.

Homesteading was part of the mythology of the Canadian frontier and there is no doubt it had an influence on defining the Canadian consciousness. For many, however, the dream proved impossible of fulfilment.

The homestead of Thomas Jamieson, taken up in 1912, and believed to be the first homestead in B.C.'s Peace River Block to be proved up. Jamieson was granted the land just prior to enlisting in 1915.

20

Where The Great Peace River Flows

1.
There's a river that is flowing toward the northern sea;
It's not famed in song and story, still it has a charm for me.
It has called me from the southland where the starry banner blows,
And I've settled down forever where the great Peace River flows.

2.
I've a little moss-chinked cabin just beyond its northern shore
Where I hope to live contented till this span of life is o'er.
May life's cares pass lightly o'er me, all its troubles and its woes
Be to me a fleeting memory where the great Peace River flows.

3.
In this little bit of Eden where the sun at midnight gleams
All our girls are just like visions from the pleasant land of dreams.
Pretty as our dainty bluebells, fair as our native rose,
They make all our lives seem brighter where the great Peace River flows.

4.
We have come from every nation, we have done our very best
To uphold the flag of Britain in this great and glorious west.
And no foeman's feet dare trample on our own true prairie rose,
'Tis the emblem of our country where the great Peace River flows.

5.

Where the great Peace River's flowing, where the pretty
  bluebell grows,
And the prairies they are glowing with the beauties of the
  rose,
Here the sun is always shining, no one sits down here
  repining
And each cloud has a silver lining where the great Peace
  River flows.

6.

When I get the final summons from the courthouse in the
  skies
From the Judge of all the Judges, may He deem it no surprise
If I ask Him just one favor—He may grant it—no one
  knows:
"Send me back beside the Rockies where the great Peace
  River flows."

"Where the Great Peace River Flows" belongs to an era in the Peace River country before the Alaska Highway, regular air lines, oil and natural gas pipelines, and immense hydroelectric development. Rather, it belongs to the beginnings of farm settlement: to the period from 1910 to 1930 when the population of the whole area rose from about 1500 to some 35,000 persons. The settler pictured in the song was typical of that period, but he was not in the mainstream of the great agricultural transformation. An understanding of who he was requires first, a look at the background to farm settlement and second, a look at the song's origins.

In the year 1900, few if any immigrants to Canada or Canadians on the move thought of the Peace River country as a place for farming. Evidence that it was good for agricultural settlement had been building for at least seventy-five years, but the fact was not generally known. Fur traders who came into the region on the heels of the North West Company explorers Alexander Mackenzie and Simon Fraser had soon found that grain and vegetables would ripen in the eighty-or-so frost free days. After the Peace River gold rush of 1862, a few miners stayed in the country, one, at least, farming for the Hudson's Bay Company. In the 1870's, botanist John Macoun, in the course of C.P.R. and geological surveys, used records from the trading-post farms to augment his own observations; he concluded that the Peace River plateau could be successfully farmed. The government of Canada recognized the long-term agricultural value of the region and, as part of the railway dealings with British Columbia, took the first steps in 1884 to acquire control of the province's Peace River Block. Interest was further stimulated in 1899 when a sample of wheat from a farm attached to a Peace River

Panoramic view of Fort St. John, 1906, six years before the country was opened to homesteaders.

mission won first prize in a Chicago grain exhibition. About the same time some of the men who had set out for the Klondike gold rush stopped in the Peace River country. One of them became the first independent farmer in the region. In the first decade of the new century, as these stories of traders, gold miners, surveyors, and missionaries became more widely known, settlers slowly began to arrive.

The settler in the song could have been one of the early squatters, or he could have taken up land after Ottawa opened the region to homesteaders in 1912. Homesteading was a settlement program in which a person could take possession of a quarter-section farm by living on the land and making certain improvements. Most of the settlers in this period were bachelors, the ratio of men to women in the whole population being about two to one. Basing his expectations on what he had heard of the country, a bachelor of his own could hope to get a subsistence living from the land. Others, following the patterns of the earlier fur traders married Indian or metis women. A last group of bachelors was more like the settlers whose wives came with them; generally more aggressive, they hoped to become substantial farmers, go south to find a wife, raise families, build schools, ensure through pressure on government that roads and railways would be extended to take their crops to market and bring some of the amenities of modern living nearer to their doors. The settler in the song seems to have been on his own and was content to remain so.

About one-half of the settlers in the early decades were born in Canada or Great Britain, one-fifth in the United States. Those from Continental Europe had in general lived for a time elsewhere in Canada or the United States. There were both young and old men among them, but many were in their thirties, and they had previously worked in a variety of jobs and professions. The area of the Peace River settlement district was 50 million acres, 3½ million of them being in the Peace River Block in British Columbia. Since one-third at most was suited to farming owing to the broken topography and the great variety of soils, settlement over the area was widely dispersed.

Because of their location some of the fertile areas never became intensively populated. Others in time became busy centers of trade and transportation. The Edmonton, Dunvegan, and British Columbia Railway, for instance, reached the town of Peace River in 1916 but did not go to Pouce Coupe and Dawson Creek until 1931. The settler in the song with his simple wants gives the impression he would choose to live where the natural vegetation holds its own, away from growing towns—in the fringe of settlement.

The song itself was probably written about 1915 by a settler who left his "little moss-chinked cabin" for military service overseas in World War I. Recollections of old timers, together with a study of the ten variant texts of the song collected up to 1972 support this view. That the type of settler persisted is indicated by a note made by a sociologist studying Peace River settlement in 1930:

> K. was found along with his dog in his windowless bachelor cabin "just thinking." He was thinking that he would be content with a small amount of cleared and broken land. He would not farm extensively like many others in the district. He just wanted enough to keep him going comfortably. His standards of comfort were decidedly elementary. Until 12 years ago this settler had been a railroader.
>
> (Dawson, C.A. *The Settlement of the Peace River Country*, Toronto, 1934 pp.241-2)

The first person to sing this song for me learnt it from such a man as this about the same year. The man lived in a cabin near the great river and got a little money to buy a few extras by selling cordwood to the stern wheeler which carried freight and passengers past his door.

Texts of the song from British Columbia and Alberta differ in interesting details. In length they average five stanzas, varying in those included. Four refer to the "flag of freedom"; three (all from B.C.) use the "flag of Britain." The place to which the settler would have the "Judge of all the Judges" return him are: Fair Alberta(4), Pouce Coupe, Taylor Crossing, and the Rockies(2). The ending of one variant

> "Take me back to old Pouce Coupe where the wine and whiskey flows"

may echo the early days in Pouce Coupe and other places when such local drinks as "Dunvegan ginger" added to the fun of the annual Dominion Day races. The places mentioned indicate the song moved from Alberta to the west. The floral emblem of Alberta, the prairie rose, is claimed indiscriminately as the emblem of "our country," which in the British Columbia texts must mean the "Peace River country."

The song appears to have become fairly widely known among both the older population and the new wave of settlers who ventured into the region at the end of World War I. Many of these people could see themselves in the person in the song who "came from the southlands where the starry banner blows" to live out his life in a simple frontier way. And nearly all who stayed in the Peace River country shared the love of the countryside, symbolized in the song by the prairie wild flowers.

21

The Banks of The Similkameen

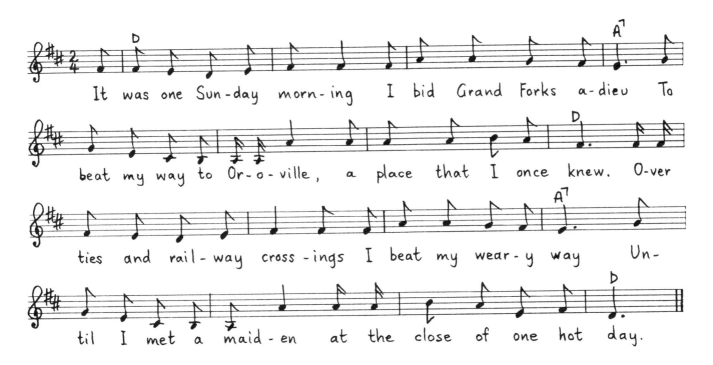

It was one Sun-day morn-ing I bid Grand Forks a-dieu To beat my way to Or-o-ville, a place that I once knew. O-ver ties and rail-way cross-ings I beat my wear-y way Un-til I met a maid-en at the close of one hot day.

1.
It was one Sunday morning I bid Grand Forks adieu
To beat my way to Oroville, a place that once I knew.
Over ties and railway crossings I beat my weary way
Until I met a maiden at the close of one hot day.

2.
"Good eve, good eve, fair maiden! My money does me no
    good:
If it hadn't a-been for the coyotes I'd a-stayed out in the
    wood."
"You're welcome, welcome, stranger, although our home
    is plain—
We ne'er have turned a stranger out on the banks of the
    Similkameen."

3.
She took me to her mother's home—she treated me
    quite well.
Her hair in dark brown ringlets about her shoulders fell.
I tried to paint her beauty, but true, it was in vain,
For perfect was the Oroville girl on the banks of the
    Similkameen.

4.
I asked her to marry me; she said it ne'er could be;
She said she had a lover, and he lived in B.C.
She said she had a lover, and true she would remain
Until he came to claim her on the banks of the
    Similkameen.

5.
So adieu, adieu, fair maiden, I never shall see no more,
But I'll never forget your kindness nor the cottage by
    the shore.
So adieu, adieu, fair maiden, I'll drink to the flowing
    stream;
I'll drink the health of the Oroville girl on the banks of
    the Similkameen.

In the late 1920's a man traveling on horseback stopped overnight at a ranch on the high rolling land of Anarchist Mountain between Osoyoos and Bridesville. After supper, with the family gathered around the coal-oil lamp in the log ranchhouse, there was some song swapping. The visitor sang a song that caught everyone's attention, for the whole family had heard the rancher sing a ballad very much like it to the same tune. The words were changed enough to catch the children's imagination. The places mentioned were now located near home, the alligators of the swamp had become coyotes in the wood, and the girl's lover, instead of being "on the sea" was now "in B.C." One of the boys learnt the words just at one hearing—his dad's song, "The Lake of Ponchartrain" had become "The Banks of the Similkameen."

The song has been collected in British Columbia a number of times: on Anarchist Mountain, at Okanagan Falls, Keremeos and Williams Lake. The journey in the ballad is always in the south Okanagan region: from Grand Forks or Keremeos to Oroville, from Penticton or Okanagan Falls to Keremeos. In Canada and the United States, earlier or other forms of the song have been reported in Alberta, New Brunswick, Vermont, Missouri, Kentucky, Michigan, Iowa and in the southwest as a cowboy song. The place names are sometimes localized. Where the song originated, no one knows, but it has been conjectured that whoever made up the original probably knew "My Little Mohea" and reversed the "plot." The sentiment of constancy and loyalty as well as the tune seem to be the song's enduring qualities.

In the British Columbia texts, especially where the girl is in Oroville, Washington, just south of the border, the fact that the lover "lives in B.C." stirs our provincial pride in an amusing way. We have felt we might have some marked virtues but are surprised to think others might really recognize them. But this is reading too much into the verse. The simple facts are that a credible rhyme was needed for an interior locality and that, since the population movement has from the early days of settlement followed the north-south direction of the Okanagan River, people in that region commonly remark that a person lives either on this or that side of the "line." Many families in the early days had relatives on both sides of the boundary.

22

Georgiana Ball

The "moose hunters" glassing for moose near Telegraph Creek, c. 1949-50. L. to r.: Bobby Ball, Thomas Dennis, Danny Marion. They wear Tahltan Indian snowshoes; Ball and Marion wear knitted ear flaps, Dennis has flaps attached to his head-gear.

Moose Hunter's Blues

As I lay here to-night in my old spruce-bough bed With thoughts of my dar-lin' go-in' round in my head, I hav-en't seen her for such a long time I won-der if she still re-mem-bers she's mine.

1.
As I lay here tonight in my old spruce-bough bed
With thoughts of my darlin' goin' round in my head—
I haven't seen her for such a long time—
I wonder if she still remembers she's mine.

2.
Now, the weather is cold and the dogs gettin' poor;
We gotta kill a moose tomorrow for sure.
Today we set runnin' a cow and a calf—
They could hear us a-comin' for a mile and a half.

3.
When we get some meat we will head into town
And dance until daylight comes rollin' around.
We'll have a good time with our sweethearts and pals
And load up our sleighs, say farewell to our gals.

4.
Now, the life of a moose hunter's sometimes quite sad,
But there's lots of good times to go with the bad;
So, if someone should tell me that I have to choose,
A million can't buy these old moose hunter's blues.

Although the Stikine watershed is isolated from both the Pacific coast and the continental interior, the Tahltan Indians, who have lived in the region from prehistoric times, very early felt the impact of Europeans on their way of life. During the first half of the nineteenth

George Ball, father of Bobby Ball who wrote the song. The guide and outfitter poses with world record stone sheep trophy taken by a client from Northern Ireland, 1931.

century, the Russians traded for furs with the Tlingit people on the coast; the Tlingit in turn recruited the Tahltans as fur-gatherers. The first direct probings of Caucasian fur traders into Tahltan territory had little effect, for the Tlingit maintained a fur monoploly. Other minor incursions came in the 1860's when a few placer miners pushed north from the Fraser River. They were soon followed by surveyors who, in the mid-1860's, mapped the route of the proposed overland telegraph which was to link North America to Europe by way of Siberia. The building of the line was abandoned before it reached the Stikine, but it did leave its name on Telegraph Creek, a small tributary of the river.

The discovery of substantial quantities of free gold near Dease Lake in 1873 precipitated an invasion of Tahltan lands which had devastating consequences. Smallpox, brought by the gold seekers—both Caucasian and Chinese—killed so many Tahltan that the remnants of their tribal groups had to unite for survival. Together about 1880 they rebuilt the village of Tahltan, situated on the Stikine some dozen miles above Telegraph Creek.

From the time of the Cassiar gold rush, Tahltan lands became easily accessible. Independent fur traders soon established themselves. They were followed by the Hudson's Bay Company, which built a trading post at Glenora, the head of Stikine navigation, some 140 miles (about 225 Km.) up the river from its mouth and 12 miles (19.2 Km.) below Telegraph Creek. In 1898, the Klondike gold rush again brought great numbers of men into the region. During both these rushes, many Tahltan acted as guides and packers. By 1900, Telegraph Creek had become the new head of navigation for the river steamers. The office of the gold commissioner was established at the new center of trade. As Glenora waned, the Hudson's Bay Company dismantled its building and moved it up the river. Before long Telegraph Creek had a hotel and a school. By 1901, the Dominion Telegraph had manned stations through the Stikine country for the telegraph line which ran from the Yukon Territory south to join the main North American systems. By this time, numbers of wealthy people seeking the heads of grizzlies and thinhorn sheep as trophies were arriving in the Stikine-Cassiar region from as far away as Europe. In response, the Tahltan added big-game guiding to their marketable talents.

During the nineteenth century, the Tahltan had, little by little, accepted new ways. Firearms replaced the bow and arrow and spear; traps supplanted snares and deadfalls; sled dogs were introduced for transportation; European fabrics, beads, and clothing were adopted; and wheat flour became a staple item of diet. From the point of view of those Tahltan who wished to maintain their cultural identity, the benefits of these innovations were outweighed by their disintegrating effects. As the stresses of outside contact continued, the elders discouraged men from marrying outside the tribe; but it appears that the marriage of Tahltan women to Caucasians who settled or worked in Tahltan territory was accepted. (See Guy Lawrence's diaries of 1904-5 in *40 Years on the Yukon Telegraph*, Vancouver, 1965.) The men from outside, when linked by marriage, were welcomed as hunting companions by their Tahltan relatives. Faced with the possibility of cultural extinction, the Tahltan seem to have accepted new ways pragmatically.

Despite the smallpox epidemic and other disruptive influences, the

Tahltan fur trapping party on the Iskut River, 100 miles south of Telegraph Creek; a Tahltan bear hunting dog, a unique breed, is coming round in front of the sled. c. 1930.

Tahltan maintained many of their traditional customs. In 1906, anthropologist G.T. Emmons reported that they led a nomadic life from September until April, trapping for furs and hunting for the larder in family camps. By June when the first salmon run began, they were back in their villages ready to catch and dry the fish. By the turn of the century, many families were customarily returning to their villages at Christmas for a short season of meeting and feasting.

Writing about 1930, the Canadian ethnologist Diamond Jenness gives the following synopsis of their annual round:

> Game is still abundant in the basin of the Stikine River, and by trapping the fur-bearing animals in winter, fishing, freighting and serving sportsmen as guides in summer, the Tahltan can live quite prosperously.
>
> (D. Jenness, *Indians of Canada*, Ottawa, 1932, pp. 375-76)

Jenness goes on to say that the people "do not thrive on the new conditions." He complains that they lack individual aggressiveness, and tend to "rely on the support and encouragement of their fellows," as if cooperation were a weakness; and his reference to hunting, so important to the subsistence of the people, is oblique.

By the early 1920's, big-game hunting had become economically important to the region. In Telegraph Creek there were three outfitters, all Caucasians, who supplied hunting parties and arranged for Tahltan guides. The first locally-based white guides appeared in the 1920's. Two Caucasians, George Adset and George Ball, who had no doubt possessed the individual drive which Diamond Jenness admired, became for years the major guides and outfitters in the region. George Ball came into the country in search of gold, worked for a time as a telegraph operator, established close relations with the Tahltan, did his first guiding in 1919 and in 1929 bought out one of the established outfitters to run his own business. Robert (Bobby) Ball followed his father's path as a guide and outfitter, and in the late 1970's continues to provide a modern guiding service in the Stikine.

Bobby Ball made up the song "The Moose Hunter's Blues" about 1949

Dennis Hyland, right, loads pack-train. He was the father of Thomas Dennis, one of the "moose hunters." c. 1925.

Big-game hunting parties have just returned to Telegraph Creek, 1928.

when he was a young man. A country-music styled song, it gives a glimpse of frontier life, which continued in the community of Telegraph Creek until the mid-1960's. Although the song is simple and direct, its story has less obvious roots. The situation which the song documents was the outcome of two generations of white and Indian people living together in mutual respect. The Caucasians had first come into the region as placer miners, but had stayed on to trap and, in two or three cases, to become big-game guides and outfitters. Their way of hunting was in the Tahltan tradition, and their companions on the trail were Tahltan.

The hunter in the song is one of a group of young men whose job was to produce fresh meat for their family groups and others during the winter, when Telegraph Creek (the town in the song) was cut off from outside supplies. Although these hunters may have sold some of the meat, their aim was primarily to provide food for the community; in this, they maintained a tradition which had long served the Tahltan people.

In winter hunting, the men made special use of their knowledge of the regular feeding and ruminating habits of the moose. To spot a moose, the hunters showshoe from their camp to a rise of land to scan the landscape for a moose rising from a period of cud-chewing. The hunt itself is a team effort. When a moose is killed, if the butchering cannot take place immediately the cleaned carcass is buried in the snow to keep it from freezing.

To those who follow the old ways, the end of a successful moose hunt is marked by preparing and eating a ritual meal. A fire is built to roast the moose's diaphragm, a marrow bone from one lower leg, and the "bum gut" or lower intestine. These are reported to be delicious, and to a grateful and hungry hunter they no doubt are. Through this meal, man and moose are bound together symbolically. G.T. Emmons reported in 1906 that his informants claimed the moose had deserted the Tahltan range from early in the nineteenth century until about 1870. The hunter's ritual first meal ensures that the moose will not again desert the people in consequence of their disrespect.

Telegraph Creek is today about the same size it was fifty years ago, but its economic base has changed radically. The fur trade has all but disappeared. After the opening of the Alaska Highway, Cassiar mining ventures were no longer dependent on traveling and freighting by way of Wrangell, Alaska, on Stikine riverboats. Not only was traffic diverted from Telegraph Creek, but development in transportation— planes, helicopters, jeeps and trucks—reduced the reliance on pack-horse trains, although several guides in the region still use them.

Telegraph Creek today has a population of about 130, representing twenty households. The nearby Indian Reserve has a further population of some 275. The main sources of income for the community are federal government payments to the reserve Indians and provincial government contracts for construction and maintenance of the Dease Lake road. Additional wealth is brought by people coming on visits, most of whom are status and non-status Tahltan. Although they were obliged to move elsewhere for employment, they always regard Telegraph Creek as home. Many make the trip to the banks of the Stikine in June and July to share in the salmon with their friends and relatives.

Transportation
By Land & Water

Notman Photographic Archives

23

Drill, Ye Tarriers, Drill

1.
Every morning at seven o'clock
You see a gang of tarriers drilling in the rock;
The foreman yells, "Now don't stand still
But come down heavy on that goddamn drill!"
Chorus
Then drill, ye tarriers, drill!
Drill, ye tarriers, drill!
For we work all day without sugar in our tay
When we work on the C.P. Railway,
So it's drill, ye tarriers, drill!

2.
The foreman's name was Pat McGann,
And b'gosh he was a damn fine man;
One day a premature blast went off
And up in the air went big Jim Gough.

3.
The gang quit work to tell his wife
How poor old Jim had lost his life;
Says she, "We'll take him into town"—
Says they, "But Jim ain't yet come down!"

88

4.
But the very next day we heard a cry,
And saw big Jim comin' from the sky.
He lit on top of a rock dump—
Says he, "Well, that's a damn hard bump!"

5.
When pay day next did come around
Big Jim a dollar short was found;
"What for?" says he: came this reply,
"You're docked for the time you were up in the sky."

6.
The boss sent us to drill a hole—
He cursed and damned our Irish soul,
He cursed the ship that brought us through
To work on the C.P. Railway crew.

7.
Our boarding-boss was from Cork's own town
And he married a widow, a "very far down."
She baked his bread and she baked it well,
And she baked it harder than the hobs o' hell.

8.
Our boarding-boss went down one day
To get some sugar to sweeten our tay.
When he came back he said it was too dear—
For he always drank his own tay clear.

9.
D.B. McDonald is our walking-boss,
And it's him that kicks up the devil's own fuss,
And if you ask him for your time
He'll send you further down the line.

10.
Now all you teamsters, you beware,
And of your horses take great care,
And when you do go to turn them round,
Don't make them go over the dumping ground.

11.
Doctor Boskin's a very fine man,
He's the lad who don't give a damn—
He'll give you three or four black pills
That will draw you over the Eagle Hills!

12.
Will Grant, our cook, was a Bluenose man
For making up hash, you bet he can.
His beans are so good they would make a fine stew
To fatten the ribs of Frank Brothers' crew.

Corey Brothers' Tunnel near what is now Palliser in the lower Kicking Horse Canyon in 1884.

In the great railway construction period of the second half of the nineteenth century, the North American railway builders' classic dictum was "Let the last mile of road pay for the next." This formula suggests that the railway paid its way as it went along — like a good corporate citizen. In fact, the railways were largely financed by land grants, money subsidies and bond guarantees provided by the various governments of the area through which the road was to run. The builders, in effect, received the railroad line as a present from the total community for managing the building of it. As the builders again and again turned out to be closely associated with government leaders, a few men using the community's land and monies entrenched themselves in the ownership of a public utility and the great power that went with it.

Elected governments encouraged railway construction for a number of reasons: first, a new railway was in those years synonymous with settlement, economic growth, and resource development; second, property-owning electors hoped to make money out of a railway-generated boom; and third, politicians and party bag-men were given large funds by railway promoters in return for the passage of favorable legislation. In this atmosphere of industrial growth, individual enterprise, and primitive democracy, political leaders often ignored the conflict between their private interest and their public responsibility. Personal fortunes were made from public railway policy by the men in government who set that policy.

The promoters in selling their railway schemes to both governments and capitalists tried to get as much money as they could. A promoter would typically present a government with as formidable a picture of the difficulties as was consistent with government optimism so that support would be generous; the capitalists, on the other hand, were attracted by glowing assurances of dividends to be creamed from an operating railroad and from any subsidiary service or resource companies. As the scheme developed, it fell upon both the government and the railway company to promote popular support. Local speculation, on however small a scale, was encouraged; people with as little as fifty or a hundred dollars to invest became participants in projected boom towns and felt they were sure to be rich in a future of expansive growth and continuing prosperity. Successful promoters, enjoying the enterprise of which they were the spark and drive, were so skilled in the manipulation of large sums of money that they themselves accumulated millions of dollars and became capitalists.

Cont.

In May, 1931, the *Vancouver Sun* requested its readers to send in as many stanzas as possible of the "old railway song," "Drill, Ye Tarriers, Drill!", for publication. Although it was an unusual request by the newspaper, hundreds of replies reportedly came by telephone and mail. Unfortunately the letters were not preserved, but on May 16, 1931, Doris S. Milligan, the staff writer given the job of sorting out the replies, was in print with a fascinating article under the banner headling: 40-YEAR-OLD MEMORIES REVIVED IN SONG OF C.P.R. CAMPS. Accompanying her story, Doris Milligan gave a tune for the chorus and her selection of stanzas saying, "The song seems to be unending and the 18 verses printed here do not pretend to be all of it." A further selection of twelve of them is presented here. In this reprint of the song, the profanity is restored, replacing the "blanks."

Of interest to folklorists tracing the origin of the song, which has wide North American circulation in a number of versions and variants, is an account in the article of a possible predecessor from the 1870's. Also, the last stanza was reportedly made up at Donald, B.C. in 1885, three years before the song was published under the authorship of Thomas F. Casey, a New York entertainer and former railroad navvy.

The chorus appeared in the paper with two variations. The line in the main text, "When we work on the Canadian Pacific Railway" became "When you're workin' on the Shuswap Railway." How many other variants there were for different railways is not recorded, but the song was sung on the Grand Trunk, the Canadian Pacific, and its southern route into British Columbia, the Crowsnest Pass Railway.

The main theme of "Drill, Ye Tarriers, Drill!" is the harsh and callous treatment of the workers. The song expresses the men's resentment of the arrogance of the foreman, the questionable deductions in pay, the poor medical treatment, and the prejudice against certain nationalities. In railway building the workers were peculiarly at a disadvantage. They were isolated and dependent on the railway for all their needs, including food and transportation if they should require or choose to leave the job.

The ill-treatment of the workers building the Crowsnest Pass line is well-documented through a Royal Commission set up in 1898 to investigate complaints. The inquiry came about only because it impinged on the immigration policies of Prime Minister Wilfred Laurier's able Minister of the Interior, the Hon. Clifford Sifton. He had encouraged men to come from Great Britain to seek employment constructing the new C.P.R. line. The findings and recommendations of the three commissioners may be found in the *Sessional Papers of the House of Commons*, Vol XXXII, No 13 (No.90a) 1898.

Fourteen years earlier, the contractors in the mountain construction of the C.P.R. near Donald faced a general strike of workers demanding pay which was nearly three months in arrears. Although conditions of work are not mentioned in the accounts, we may assume they were not unlike those found on the Crowsnest Pass line. James Ross, who was in charge of construction, called upon Captain Steele of the N.W.M.P., who was ill and in bed, to be prepared for a fight, aided by company men to be sworn in as specials. The strike leaders were arrested but not before a man was shot. In the story as it has come down to us, Sam Steele stands as a hero, but he, in fact, was doing the company's bidding and not impartially maintaining law and order. William

Mackenzie and Donald Mann, who turn up elsewhere in this book, were involved in this dispute. On the Crowsnest Pass Railway the contractors acted without any semblance of police authority.

To return to the song, Doctor Boskin's black pills were, of course, laxatives, a common prescription of a hurried or incompetent physician. The Eagle Hills may simply be the slopes along Eagle Pass. An incomplete quatrain printed in the paper reads:

> We are tearing down the mountains and blowing up the rocks
> And they charge us a dollar for a ten-cent pair of socks.

Through the End of Track commissary, contractors retrieved the money they had paid to the men.

D.B. Macdonald was a contractor on the C.P.R. Lake Superior North Shore about 1885. Finally, Frank Brothers, a foreman track layer, was the man who replaced the spike that Donald Smith bent on his first attempt to drive home the "last spike."

St. Mary's Bridge, B.C., April, 1898. The Royal Commission was tabling its report as they worked.

Two of the most successful and scandalous railway builders and promoters appeared in the late history of North American railway building: they were Sir William Mackenzie and Sir Donald Mann, and they were both involved directly in situations in British Columbia which gave rise to two songs in this book. One song, "Where the Fraser River Flows," relates to railroad construction on their Canadian Northern Pacific Railway in 1912. The other song, "Bowser's Seventy-Twa," played a part in the confrontation in 1912 between the Vancouver Island coal mine owners — headed by Mackenzie and Mann — and the coal miners. Mackenzie and Mann, wearing the three faces of promoter, contractor and capitalist, are models of a type of developer who marked (or marred) the early years of this century in British Columbia.

William Mackenzie and Donald Mann, both from Ontario, met while building the C.P.R. and, in 1886, became partners in a contracting firm. They were best known as railway builders, but in all their enterprises Mackenzie's talent in raising money was paramount. Although in 1911 they both received knighthoods, within two years their financial manipulations were being exposed and attacked in the Canadian parliament. They were accused of siphoning off money from their government-backed bonds and from government funding to use in their extensive business empire. R.E. Gosnell, in a long footnote on the pair, after crediting them with expanding a 100-mile rail line into the 12,000-mile Canadian Northern Railway system, reports that, in addition,

> Mackenzie and Mann have promoted, and control, a great many other enterprises of diversified character — the Toronto and Winnipeg street railway systems; the Electric Development Company of Ontario (which has immense works at Niagara); the Sao Paulo Tramway, Light and Power Company; the Rio de Janeiro Tramway, Light and Power Company; the Atikokan Iron Company; the Moose Mountain iron Mines, Ltd.; the Canadian (Dunsmuir) Collieries Company, Ltd.; the Pacific Whaling Company; and the Western Canadian Lumber Company, besides being interested in many Canadian and other enterprises of importance.
>
> *(A History of British Columbia, Part Two,* Victoria, 1913, p. 172)

24

Freight wagons at Wright's Ranch—127 Mile House—at Lac La Hache.

Teaming Up The Cariboo Road

Here comes Hen-ry Cur-rie, He's al-ways in a hur-ry, Team-ing up the Car-i-boo Road. He makes his hors-es go Through the dust and through the snow, Team-ing up the Car-i-boo Road. You should see him sprin-tin' To the ball at Clin-ton, Team-ing up the Car-i-boo Road. He makes the lad-ies prance, Just like his hor-ses dance, Team-ing up the Car-i-boo Road.

Chorus:

When you hear that whip a-pop-pin', You bet he's got a load. When you

hear that sweet voice sing-ing, "Stand up row-dy on the Car-i-boo Road!"

1.
Here comes Henry Currie,
He's always in a hurry,
Teaming up the Cariboo Road.
He makes his horses go
Through the dust and through the snow,
Teaming up the Cariboo Road.
You should see him sprintin'
To the ball at Clinton,
Teaming up the Cariboo Road.
He makes the ladies prance,
Just like his horses dance,
Teaming up the Cariboo Road.

Chorus
When you hear that whip a-poppin',
You bet he's got a load.
When you hear that sweet voice singing,
"Stand up rowdy on the Cariboo Road!"

2.
Pete Egan as a rule
To his horses he is cruel,
Teaming up the Cariboo Road.
He beats them with a rail,
Puts fire in their tail,
Teaming up the Cariboo Road.
Old Pete he looks so wicked
When you ask him for a ticket,
Teaming up the Cariboo Road.
At the sight of half-a-dollar
He will grab you by the collar,
Teaming up the Cariboo Road.

3.
The driver's on the deck
With a rag around his neck,
Teaming up the Cariboo Road.
While the swamper in the stable
Makes sure the teams are able,
Teaming up the Cariboo Road.
When the roads are in a mire,
Then the freighters earn their hire,
Teaming up the Cariboo Road,
But they can beat the weather
When they all pull together,
Teaming up the Cariboo Road.

This Cariboo Road freight outfit was operated by H.H. Sing, a Chinese teamster.

B.C. Provincial Archives

The original Cariboo wagon road, built between 1862 and 1865, joined Yale at the head of navigation on the lower Fraser River to Barkerville, the largest community in Cariboo's goldfields. The road penetrated a mountain barrier which till then had barely yielded a mule trail to the miners and made the remote diggings accessible to freight wagon and stage coach. The most remarkable part of its four hundred tortuous miles was that chiselled from and shored up along the precipitous walls of the Fraser Canyon.

The name "Cariboo Road" has continued from the early days to suggest risk, adventure, and heroic achievement. Although the road has gone through several phases as new modes of transportation and road building have been introduced, the historic label remains. Today the section of Highway 97 from Cache Creek to Prince George is posted as the "Cariboo Highway." Several major changes have left few traces of the old wagon road, but place names, landmarks, and land forms still remind us of its story.

The first big change came less than twenty years after the wagon road's completion. Canadian Pacific Railroad construction in the early 1880's destroyed or badly damaged much of the old road along the Fraser Canyon from Yale to Lytton. Ashcroft on the Thompson River became the junction of road and rail, the transfer point to the trunk road serving the ranching and mining country to the north. To make the link to the old road, a bridge led from Ashcroft across the river to a new route up Bonaparte Creek to Clinton.

Cont.

The song "Teaming Up the Cariboo Road" dates from those years after the railroad came through. The persons mentioned in the song were actual teamsters; Henry Currie drove freight extras for the "B.X." line. In addition to the freight wagons, the Ashcroft-Barkerville road carried weekly stage coaches. The country was still sparsely settled and neighbors often remote. To break the isolation of winter, people within a day or two's wagon travel of Clinton came to a great mid-winter get together known as "the Ball." They filled every stable, barn and bit of space in the small community, danced all night, and often stayed for several days. "Teaming Up the Cariboo Road" was no doubt heard at the Ball during those years around the turn of the century.

The coming of the motor car made necessary a re-thinking of the road policies of British Columbia. After World War I, surveys were made of new road-beds with suitable grading and safety conditions for the automobile. In 1926 road builders began to rebuild the road destroyed by C.P.R. construction. By 1928 the southwest corner of the Province was again connected by road to the upper Fraser regions. The New Cariboo Road, as it was called, ran 414 miles from Yale to Prince George.

The present phase of the Cariboo Road was brought about for both technological and economic reasons. Giant machines developed for road building during World War II enabled "cut-and-fill" techniques to be applied to highway construction on an unprecedented scale. Since all the bridges built in the mid-1920's were purposely designed for a twenty-five year life span, they had to be replaced or removed by about 1950. Designers of replacements were aware that the growing trucking industry needed suitable roads. Thus, by 1950, provincial and federal highway planners had shaped a wide and less tortuous route for the northern and southern sections of the Cariboo Road. In some ninety years, the wagon road was transformed into parts of two national highways, Highways 1 and 97.

Freight wagons on Cariboo Road near Ashcroft, c. 1900.

Where The Fraser River Flows

Fel-low Work-ers, pay at-ten-tion to what I'm going to men-tion, For it is the fixed in-ten-tion of the Work-ers of the World — And I hope you'll all be read-y, true-heart-ed, brave and stead-y — To gath-er round our stan-dard when the Red Flag is un-furled. Where the

Chorus:

Fras-er Riv-er flows, each fel-low work-er knows They have bul-lied and op-pressed us, but still our un-ion grows; And we're going to find a way, boys, for short-er hours and bet-ter pay, boys; We're

going to win the day, boys, where the Fras-er Riv-er flows!

1.

Fellow workers, pay attention to what I'm going to mention
For it is the fixed intention of the Workers of the World—
And I hope you'll all be ready, true-hearted, brave and steady,
To gather round our standard when the Red Flag is unfurled.

Chorus

Where the Fraser River flows, each fellow worker knows
They have bullied and oppressed us, but still our union grows;
And we're going to find a way, boy, for shorter hours and better pay, boys,
We're going to win the day, boys, where the Fraser River flows!

2.

Now these "gunny sack" contractors have all been dirty actors;
They're not our benefactors, each fellow worker knows.
So we've got to stick together in fine or dirty weather;
We will show no white feather where the Fraser River flows.

3.

Now, the boss the law is stretching, bulls and pimps he's fetching;
They are a fine collection, as Jesus only knows.
But why their mothers reared them, and why the devil spared them
Are questions we can't answer where the Fraser River flows.

This poster, though not of Wobbly origin, hung for many years in Vancouver's I.W.W. Hall on Cordova Street.

96

"Where the River Shannon Flows," a 1905 product of Tin Pan Alley, had a steady popularity for many years; and it is not surprising that in a land of great rivers like British Columbia adaptations appeared. Two versions of the song developed, one for the Peace, the other for the Fraser River. The Fraser song led to variants for the Skeena and Lardeau Rivers. The Peace River song (No. 20) started in Alberta and migrated up-river into British Columbia. "Where the Fraser River Flows" originated in British Columbia where its author, Joe Hill, came to rally support for the construction workers building the Canadian Northern Pacific Railway through the Fraser Canyon and up the Thompson River. Hill, an immigrant to the United States, believed all working men should unite to make a better world; to this end, he ignored the international boundary and came to assist his fellows who were standing up for their rights.

Industrial Worker Feb. 13, 1913

"Why should workers produce for idlers?"

"Where the Fraser River Flows" was first sung in British Columbia in 1912 during the two-and-a-half month strike on the Canadian Northern (later Canadian National) Railway. According to government reports, a total of six thousand men downed their tools. The men were strung out along 160 miles of right-of-way. How did they unite? *The Industrial Worker*, an I.W.W. union paper, carried this story shortly after the strike began:

> . . . the main thing that caused the walkout was the foul condition of the camps in which the men were herded. . . . In one of the Tierney camps the bunks were built three tiers high and the men after waking each morning for a short time, with raging headaches, tore down the top bunk. . . . In other camps the floors were laid directly upon the ground instead of 18 inches above, insufficient air space was allowed and wash houses, dry houses and bath houses were of the vilest sort. . . . The strike broke out on the 27th in Nelson and Benson's camp no. 4. . . . The men came down the line and called all men out at camps 3 and 2. A meeting was held at I.W.W. hall in Lytton and demands were formulated, various committees elected and in a short time the entire line from Hope to Kamloops was tied up, over 4,200 men being directly involved. . . .

They also wanted increased wages. But nothing would have happened without organization.

Who then were the organizers? They belonged to the Industrial Workers of the World, a revolutionary union founded in Chicago in 1905 when a number of industrial unions, with the support of the foremost socialist theorists of the United States, joined together. The great plan of the I.W.W. was to organize American society into some dozen industrial departments comprising unions of all the working men and women. The people, by voting and working through their unions, would choose the government of the country. Once enough support was organized through the big union, the alternate government it had created would become the only effective government in the land. The conflict between Capital, as seen in the great money trusts and syndicates, and Labor, would disappear in a classless society. Their dream was of a world free of war, unemployment and poverty; one of their slogans shows the extent of their hope:

> All workers of one industry in one union; all unions of workers in one big labor alliance the world over.

First I.W.W. charter in Canada: Vancouver, B.C., 1906.

Author photo

Their banner was a simple red flag, which had been a rallying symbol of labor from the days of the Roman Empire.

In British Columbia the first I.W.W. charter was issued in May 1906, seventeen months after the founding meeting. Between 1911 and 1913 there were at one time nine I.W.W. locals in existence in British Columbia. They led six strikes involving some ten thousand railway and other workers. Their effect on construction jobs is described by G.R. Stevens in *Canadian National Railways*:

> In a matter of months it became impossible to drive pick-and-shovel men as in the past; the fists and axe handles of the straw boss no longer were effective instruments of persuasion.

Stevens goes on to describe the 1912 Fraser River railway workers' strike:

> It was an orderly affair: the men left the right-of-way and established their own "mulligan camps" in the bush. Petitions by the strikers to the Dominion and provincial governments led to certain minor improvements in the camps and in some instances to slight wage increases. ... The popularity of a contractor often led to quick and satisfactory settlements, or his unpopularity to defiant holdouts. ... The dignity of labour ... had become (in some instances at least) a factor in employee-management relations.

Stevens does not mention that the provincial government paid out over $7,000 for special police. The Dominion government reported the strike ended in favor of the employers.

The Fraser River railway workers struck because the men had specific and tangible complaints. Behind the difficulties were the financial policies of the classic railroad builders, Sir William MacKenzie and Sir Donald Mann.

In "Where the Fraser River Flows" the immediate employers are referred to contemptuously as "gunny-sack" contractors: i.e. the sub-contractors were seen as being poorly financed, skimping to the point of inefficiency and workers' hardship, and apparently such bad managers that they would quite likely face bankruptcy. What could not be known generally by the workers was that any sub-contractor undertaking to build for MacKenzie and Mann was in a poor situation. The fact was that both the workers and the sub-contractors were getting a meagre portion of the money that the public, through government guaranteed securities, had given MacKenzie and Mann for the railway construction. And even that portion was handled in such a way that small contractors did face bankruptcy; their banks demanded repayment of loans made on the strength of the contracts. Thus the real cash came not from MacKenzie and Mann but from the banks; it was this money that paid for the actual labor and materials used in laying out and leveling the road bed and laying the track. By the end of 1913 MacKenzie and Mann owed British Columbia contractors $7,500,000. They were soon in Ottawa pleading "no funds" and asking the Dominion government to bail them out.

MacKenzie and Mann produced a 9,300 mile railway system. They "wheeled and dealed" but never put any of their own money into construction. To prevent interference in their complex financial operations, they kept all the voting shares in their railway company for themselves. Another of their devices was to adopt a number of corporate names to handle a chain of money transactions. Their three top names in British Columbia were: The Canadian Northern Pacific Railway; MacKenzie and Mann Co., Ltd.; and Northern Construction Company. It was as if they had three pockets: the government arranged to put money into pocket one, the C.N.P.R.; MacKenzie and Mann then transferred it first to pocket two, and then to pocket three. Next they went again to the government with pocket one empty. If pressed by the suspicious, they would show that pocket two was empty also. This process apparently worked again and again. Both men became very wealthy.

In May 1914, when trying to get a total of $45,000,000 from the Dominion government, MacKenzie and Mann came up against the Member for Calgary, R.B. Bennett, who many years later became Prime Minister of Canada. He broke with the government and led the attack against further give-aways. After commenting on "the contractors who have been swarming around the hotel corridors in Ottawa... because [MacKenzie and Mann] would not pay them" he typified their operations in these words:

> To own a construction company, a railroad company, and a good reliable printing press is better than your own mint. Nothing can limit your fortune but the extent of your greed.

Although 80% of the $45,000,000 was to pay debts and finish the construction in British Columbia, no member from the province introduced the issue of social injustice fostered by such practices. Bennett's morality in 1914 extended to the honor of paying one's debts, but not to workers' rights.

The strike, the unpaid contractors, bribery of government leaders, and rising unemployment soured the people of British Columbia on the "great railway boom." The Gold Brick Twins, McBride and Bowser, were shortly to leave their positions of leadership in British Columbia. McBride resigned; and Bowser, while retaining his seat in the next provincial election in 1916, saw his party's representation cut by three-quarters as the people finally rejected a regime which lived off inflated public expectations, private patronage, and corruption.

Construction workers on the C.N. P.R.. The Canadian Northern became part of the government-owned Canadian National Railway.

B.C. Provincial Museum

26

P.G.E. Railway # 3 built in 1914.   B.C. Provincial Archives

The P.G.E. Song

1.
Up in that far north country where the skies are always
   blue,
They're waiting for the happy day when the P.G.E. goes
   through.
The squawfish will be squawking and the moose will
   start to moo,
The grizzly bears will grizzle when the P.G.E. goes
   through.

Chorus
Oh, Lord! I know my toil will end
When I hear that whistle coming round the bend.

2.
They say that all the members of Urquart's survey crew
Will be working on the extra gang when the P.G.E. goes
   through.
Bill Herlihy, he's got a squaw, her name is Buckskin Sue,
They're going on the trapline when the P.G.E. goes
   through.

3.

The hornets build their little nests up in the spruce and
   pine,
They love to sting the axemen who are cutting out the
   line.
So if the railroad bends a bit like railroads shouldn't do,
Just blame it on the hornets when the P.G.E. goes
   through.

4.

When running line on snowshoes, the snow got very
   deep,
Old Ab Richman, he dug a hole, crawled in and went to
   sleep.
The snow blew in and covered him, but we know what
   to do—
We'll dig him out in springtime when the P.G.E. goes
   through.

"The P.G.E. Song" was made in 1949 by Keith Crowe, then a member
of a survey crew at Summit Lake, north of Prince George. Railway surveys had been made in the same area as early as 1913 but still there
were no tracks. There were no tracks south of Prince George to
Quesnel and none between Squamish and North Vancouver. The last
line of the chorus of the song, "When I hear that whistle coming round
the bend," is an ironic expression of the long-suffering hope of
people living along unbuilt portions of the Pacific Great Eastern
Railway. The railway from a short time after it was begun in 1912 had
become an exasperating symbol of railway bungling. Over the years
the initials P.G.E. were variously expanded to such nicknames as
Promoters Get Everything, Provincial Government Expense, Please Go
Easy, Past God's Endurance, and Prince George Eventually.

The Pacific Great Eastern Railway was conceived in its first phase as
linking North Vancouver to Fort George; this would open up a new
area of the province to continental and world markets by rail and sea.
The port and rail facilities on Burrard Inlet would be joined with the
main line of the Grand Trunk Pacific at its boom town of Fort George
(which became Prince George in 1915). Not only did the proposed
Fort George terminal offer access to the new port of Prince Rupert and
to the mineral, grain resources and manufacturing centers to the east,
but Fort George would be the starting point for rail extensions to the
Peace River country to the northeast and eventually to the Yukon
Territory. P.G.E. construction under the conditions of its government
agreement was to be completed in three years, on July 1, 1915. But
through a long and complicated series of circumstances it was not
completed until 1952.

The P.G.E. was begun towards the end of the great railroad building
era. In the public mind railways were the key to settlement and
resource development, but to promoters they were a way of making
money. The principals and promoters of two big railway interests
reaching into British Columbia in the first decade of this century—the
British-owned Grand Trunk and the American-based Great
Northern—had both examined the possibilities of making money
from a railway on the route generally followed by the P.G.E. and had
backed off. It was poor ground for speculators; there was no bonanza
of immediately exploitable resources in the Chilcotin or Cariboo.

How then did the P.G.E. get started? The public had been thoroughly
sold on railway construction as a guarantee of prosperity—and not
just by statesmanlike assurances that the building and financing of
such projects were wise policies. In the 1909 election Sir Richard
McBride and Attorney-General William Bowser had paraded their
railway accomplishments: the Grand Trunk was well under way, the
Canadian Northern Pacific would be built if they were re-elected.

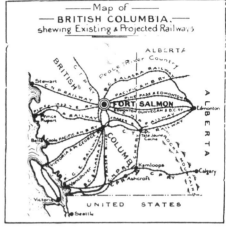

British Columbia Magazine, March, 1913

P.G.E. Railway construction north
of Prince George. c. 1954.

Author photo

Government Offices and Court House at Stewart

STEWART, B.C.
The Most Central Port of British Columbia

Have you read of the Groundhog Mountain Anthracite Coal Deposit?

Have you realized its extent and value, 84 per cent fixed carbon?

Have you recognized its proximity to Stewart, only 96 miles. The projected Canadian Northern Eastern Railway will tap these deposits?

Have you ever lived in a coaling port?

Have you ever lived in a mining town?

Have you ever lived in a transcontinental terminus?

Have you grasped the tremendous significance of a town embodying all three?

Have you invested in Stewart? If not, why not? Now is your chance while the town is young. Buy before everyone else does and prices have advanced.

We have Lots for Sale
from $400.00 and up

STEWART LAND CO. LIMITED
Head Office: 101-2 Pemberton Block, Victoria, B.C.   P.O. Box 575
Fifth Street, Stewart, B.C.   P.O. Box J, Phone 25

Author photo

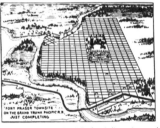

FORT FRASER
The Hub of B.C. on the G.T.P.

FORT FRASER TOWNSITE ON THE GRAND TRUNK PACIFIC R.R. JUST COMPLETING

Note Fort Fraser directly on the Grand Trunk Pacific main line at the east end of Fraser Lake.

Note the junction of the Upper and Lower Nechaco rivers touching Fraser Lake at Fort Fraser, affording over one thousand miles of navigable waterway.

Note, in addition to the Grand Trunk Pacific survey, numerous trails leading into Fort Fraser from almost every direction, some indicating other proposed railway surveys.

Note its location in the very centre of the largest and richest agricultural and mineral section of British Columbia, embracing the Stuart Lake country, Nechaco Valley, Blackwater country, Endako Valley, Ootsa Lake country, Bulkley Valley, and the Babine country.

Note the townsite of Fort Fraser is all paid for, and we hold an indefeasible title. The property has been surveyed and duly registered.

Note that fortunes are being made by shrewd investors in real estate all over the great Canadian West. Vancouver did not even have a railway siding in 1885, yet A. G. Ferguson, Esq., bought lots on Hastings Street, Vancouver, twenty years ago at $700. These lots in ten years were worth $20,000, and today cannot be bought for less than $135,000. Prince Rupert had no railroad in 1907, and yet Robert Ross, who bought on May 24, 1909, lots 18 and 19, block 6, section 1, Prince Rupert, for $600, sold them October 17, 1911, for $5,000. Similar instances may be cited in Winnipeg, Calgary, Lethbridge, Edmonton, Regina and Moose Jaw.

Note that the price paid for a Fort Fraser lot is not paid for land alone—it is paid for opportunity. Opportunities attract population, and population makes land values.

Be alert, investigate now while prices are $500 per lot and up, and terms 10 per cent, cash and balance $15 per month without interest or taxes. Attractive and instructive literature and prices will be supplied on request.

Dominion Stock & Bond Corporation, Limited
Winch Building, Hastings Street   .   .   .   Vancouver, B.C.

They told their audiences as they campaigned throughout the province "that the bringing in of these railways would *double the price of real estate.*" The electors were told to "get in, boys, on the city lots and acreage adjoining the projected railways, as you will never again have such an opportunity." The voters were co-opted as speculators. When the legislation for the P.G.E. was under discussion in February 1912, this same fervour for speculation was abroad. North Vancouver was to have its new railroad; Vancouver would soon have another transcontinental terminal on completion of the Canadian Northern Pacific; real estate was booming. McBride called an election at the end of February and on March 1 announced with buoyant confidence that the P.G.E. agreement had been signed and sealed. The great majority of voters welcomed the news and uncritically returned McBride and Bowser, the "Gold Brick Twins," at the head of a landslide which gave the Conservatives all but two of the forty-two legislative seats. What kind of deal McBride and Bowser had made with the railway builders would only come to light after the P.G.E. faltered. While government-backed funds were spent freely, the mileage of tracks was far behind schedule. The P.G.E. was not in difficulty alone; on the Canadian Northern Pacific sub-contractors were not getting paid and could not pay their work gangs and their own supply bills. Charges were made of greedy and cynical handling of public monies by a clique of promoters, contractors and politicians. Under the load of these accusations the old Bowser-McBride machine broke down. In the 1916 provincial election the people turned to the Liberals who on forming the government held an enquiry into the affairs of the P.G.E. The upshot was that there had been political mismanagement and graft, and that the builder-contractors had made a lot of money. The people of British Columbia had paid heavily and would continue to pay for a railroad that for over thirty years went "from nowhere to nowhere."

Messrs. Foley, Welch and Stewart paid back $1,000,000 of the $6,000,000 they had "legally swindled" and continued to operate construction companies, although they had diversified into such firms as Bloedel, Stewart & Welch in the lumber industry. For years they were remembered along the route of the Grand Trunk Pacific, later part of the C.N.R., as "Frig 'em, Work 'em and Starve 'em" for their notorious gouging of the construction workers in the years prior to the P.G.E. episode when they were building the G.T.P.

The provincial government took over the P.G.E. in 1918 after much litigation. The two ends of the proposed initial phase of the road were finally completed in 1952 and in 1956 the rails finally reached the Peace River with the terminals at Dawson Creek and Fort St. John. In 1922 the partial road then in operation lost about $2,000,000 for the year and had a total debt of $26,000,000. In 1972 the books reported an operations profit of nearly $1,000,000 but the total debt was $259,000,507.

On April 1, 1972 under the government of W.A.C. Bennett the name of the railway was changed to the British Columbia Railway. The railway construction continues further north but looking at the total balance sheet it is still P.G.E.—Provincial Government Expense.

102

Minto *between the Upper and Lower Arrow Lakes, c. 1949.*

27

The *Minto*

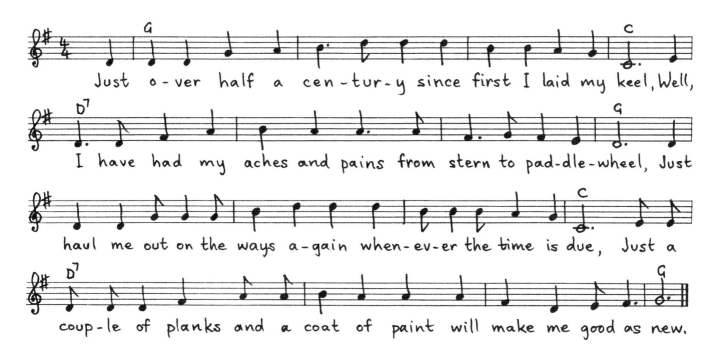

Just o-ver half a cen-tur-y since first I laid my keel, Well, I have had my aches and pains from stern to pad-dle-wheel, Just haul me out on the ways a-gain when-ev-er the time is due, Just a coup-le of planks and a coat of paint will make me good as new.

1.
Just over half a century since first I laid my keel,
Well, I have had my aches and pains from stern to
  paddlewheel,
Just haul me out on the ways again whenever the time is
  due,
Just a couple of planks and a coat of paint will make me
  good as new.

2.
Deline my run, as ordered, from Robson to Arrowhead,
My sisters are all in the boneyard; they're broken up and
  dead,
Well, I know that paddlewheelers are far between and
  few,
Just a couple of planks and Bob at the wheel will make
  me good as new.

3.
I have seen the high and the haughty and I know the
  rich and broke,
I know the trapper with his pelts, the miner and his
  poke,
I know the lusty logger; what a roisting, boisterous
  crew!
Just a couple of planks and Bob at the wheel will make
  me good as new.

4.
I know the river's romance and I tasted Heaven and Hell,
I think of all the bygone days and what my staterooms
  tell;
Who says I'm due for the boneyard? Not the captain or
  the crew,
Just a couple of planks and Bob at the wheel—you'll
  make me good as new.

5.
Now I hate to leave the Arrow Lakes and I hate to say
    goodbye—
Oh, please, someone, rescue me, 'fore I'm high and dry!
I'd like to serve you once again with my captain and my
    crew,
Just a couple of planks and Bob at the wheel will make
    me good as new.

For over a century paddlewheelers played a vital role in British Columbia. These steamships, both sidewheelers, like the Hudson's Bay Company's *S.S. Beaver,* and sternwheelers, like the C.P.R.'s *S.S. Moyie,* have become museum pieces, symbols of the periods in which they flourished. The *S.S. Beaver* is with us now only in replica, but the *S.S. Moyie* herself, who ended her work in 1957, the last of her kind, is well preserved as a museum of local history at Kaslo on Kootenay Lake.

The sternwheelers served gold seekers, settlers, railroad builders and miners. The waterways they plied included the Fraser-Thompson and Columbia systems (both rivers and lakes), the Skeena and Stikine Rivers, Bennett Lake of the upper Yukon system, and the Peace River. They were at the same time both freighters and elegant passenger vessels.

Sternwheelers, with their flat bottoms and shallow drafts, were in their time the ideal workhorses for these waterways; a skilled master could take one through white water and treacherous currents and make a landing almost anywhere. When the hull was damaged, the wooden planks were readily replaced. Captains often became heroic figures to the communities they served.

The *S.S. Minto,* a medium-sized vessel 162 feet long by 32 feet wide, was built by the C.P.R. in Nakusp on the Arrow Lakes in 1898. She served Arrow Lakes mining communities and also linked the two C.P.R. tracks which came west through the Rockies by the Kicking Horse and Crow's Nest passes. The *Minto* worked first as a winter ship in the shallow water and ice, yielding to a larger vessel for the summers; but, in a service maintained reluctantly by the C.P.R. owing to the onset of the Great Depression, from 1932 she worked year round. After World War II modes of transportation shifted from rail and river-boats to road, trucks, ferries and air with the result that the *Minto* made her last run from Robson to Arrowhead in 1954.

People who had known this old sternwheeler all or most of their lives felt that somehow the ship should be kept going or at least receive some special treatment. Amid a welter of sentiment, Nakusp's Chamber of Commerce bought her for one dollar. During discussions on her fate and attempts to raise funds for whatever project was undertaken, the song "The *Minto*" was created. Some people wanted her afloat with Bob Manning still her skipper. Others saw her as a museum, but since no money was forthcoming, she was sold for some $700 to be scrapped. Thus, after 56 years' service and a short time on the beach, the end of the *Minto* had surely come.

As the salvage company sold the *Minto's* fittings, John Nelson, 76 years of age and a lover of the Lake boats, determined that she should not end up a rotting, discarded hulk. He purchased her for $800 and had her towed to the foreshore of his farm property at Galena Bay, hoping to restore her as a museum despite her loss of paddlewheel, boiler, engine and generator. In the very high water of 1961, Nelson floated the *Minto* to a sandy level which could have been her last site but for the building of the storage dam at the south end of the Arrow Lakes. The High Arrow Dam (officially named for Hugh L. Keenleyside in 1969) was a condition of the 1961 Columbia River Treaty. As the water rose behind the new dam, there was still talk of saving the ship, but the price of replacing her now dry-rotted timbers and restoring her as a museum was estimated by a marine engineer at $100,000.

John Nelson, who died in 1967, was spared seeing the *Minto's* end. His son Walter decided that if the *Minto* were not to be restored, she should be burned, joining many old lakeside landmarks caught by the dammed waters. In the summer of 1968 when the *Minto* was towed out onto the lake, she carried this message on her bow: "Au revoir *Minto*—but not forgotten." Walter Nelson lit the flame of the funeral pyre.

John Nelson bought the partly gutted Minto *from a salvage company but died in 1967 before he could realize his dreams of refitting the vessel as a museum. His son, Walter, seeing no practical alternative, joined in the burning of the deteriorated hulk. At exactly 12 noon on August 1, 1968, he lit the flame of the funeral pyre.*

B.C. Hydro

28

Alberta Provincial Archives

The Fort Nelson Freighter's Song

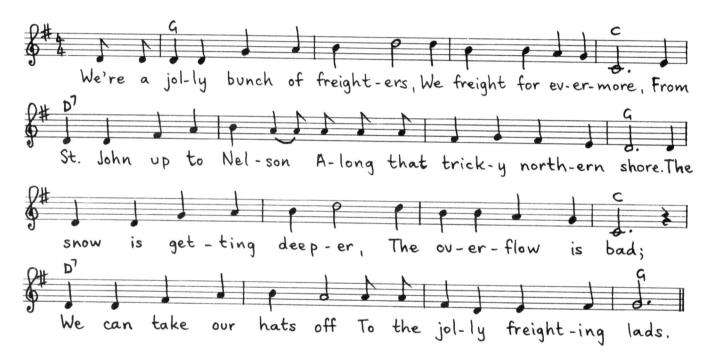

We're a jol-ly bunch of freight-ers, We freight for ev-er-more, From St. John up to Nel-son A-long that trick-y north-ern shore. The snow is get-ting deep-er, The ov-er-flow is bad; We can take our hats off To the jol-ly freight-ing lads.

1.
We're a jolly bunch of freighters,
We freight for evermore,
From St. John up to Nelson
Along that tricky northern shore.
The snow is getting deeper,
The overflow is bad;
We can take our hats off
To the jolly freighting lads.

Chorus
Oh, listen to the jingle,
The rumble and the roar,
As we come a-gliding
Down the old Fort Nelson shore!
Our faces are frostbitten,
We freight for the H.B.C.;
If you don't think we get there on time,
Just ask the Company!

2.
Now Gus he takes the tail end—
The reason you'll know why—
For Walter Weldon's horses
Won't pull; they'd sooner die.
Lena hollers, "Sandy!"
She whips him on the tail,
But Sandy never speeds up,
Or does he ever fail.

3.
Bill Pickell's getting weary
Of punching overflow,
His dainty prancing horses
Are getting awfully slow.
All night he sits and schemes and plans
To keep from breaking trail,
For they might get their feet wet,
Or water on their tails!

Today Fort Nelson is a railway terminus and a main stop on an international highway; it is served by bus and plane. Before the Alaska Highway mastered the land barriers in 1941 and before the bush pilots of the 1930's leaped them, this Hudson's Bay Trading Post on the Nelson River was very difficult of access. The "Fort Nelson Freighter's Song," with its doughty sleighmen, comes from the 1930's when the character of Fort Nelson was still closely tied to its nineteenth century past.

The first Fort Nelson had been a Nor'Wester's trading post until it was attacked in 1812 and its occupants killed by Indians who resented the traders' intrusion into their territory. For fifty years it was abandoned until in 1865 the Hudson's Bay Company built again at the site. It subsequently became an important trading post, its trade goods and furs being carried on the Nelson and Liard Rivers to Fort Simpson. When settlement of the Peace River District brought rail and river transport near enough, a route south became possible. In 1925 a Hudson's Bay Company man blazed a trail 250 miles over rock and muskeg between Fort St. John and Fort Nelson. Trying to convey to his readers the remoteness of Fort Nelson in the mid-1930's, H. Glynn Ward in *The Wide World* (London, Sept. 1938) wrote the following:

Bill Pickell's outfit on the Beatton River, north of Fort St. John, on the way to Fort Nelson, 1932.

> To understand more correctly the isolation of the place, you must realize that the distance between Fort Nelson and the nearest Trading Post at Fort St. John is almost the length of Scotland, with wild muskeg country in between. Setting out from Fort St. John, a man must go tirelessly afoot for 30 days, over country desperately hard and wet, following mostly old trap-line trails, to reach Fort Nelson. In winter it is a little easier, for you can travel the frozen rivers, the Beatton, the Sikanni, and the Nelson, for three weeks by dog team, five weeks by horse-drawn sleigh. But an airplane will cover the distance in two hours.

Hudson's Bay Company store, Fort Nelson, C. 1935.

The Company store in the 1930's kept goods of all sorts which they traded mainly for furs. One report lists "kegs of nails, barrels of lard, thick striped Hudson's Bay blankets, bright coloured dresses and shawls, guns, ammunition, sacks of flour and cereals, canned foods, candles," everything "from moccassins to marmalade."

Another list of Fort Nelson trade goods adds beans, tea, coffee, sugar, salt, traps, snares, and stoves. The goods were brought to Fort St. John by truck and then loaded onto the sleighs in racks made of lumber. Although the bulk of the goods was freighted to Fort Nelson, traders along the way were also supplied. As each load arrived at its destination, the racks were left behind to be used for boar building. Some of the goods was destined for the forty people living in the vicinity of Fort Nelson, but most of it would be boated down the river after the spring thaw to be traded along the shores, some of it reaching the Mackenzie River delta.

A freight party might start out with as many as ten teams of horses. One sleigh was often fitted with a caboose for cooking. In the last stanza the phrase "punching overflow" refers to the problem created by the "overflow" of water which at times breaks through the river ice and runs through the snow. As it freezes onto the sleigh runners, it widens the runners and makes pulling more difficult. If the slush which freezes onto the horses' feet is left there too long, the horses' legs will freeze.

107

29

Public Archives of Canada

The Wreck Of The *C.P. Yorke*

Oh, come all ye ship-mates and lis-ten to me, To a stor-y that will make you grieve, Of a tug that went down off Tat-ten-ham Ledge, 'Twas on a Christ-mas Eve.

1.
Oh, come all ye shipmates and listen to me,
To a story that will make you grieve,
Of a tug that went down off Tattenham Ledge,
'Twas on a Christmas Eve.

2.
The *C.P. Yorke* she was headin' north,
She was headin' north for Duncan Bay,
And, though 'twas the mate that stood watch at her
     wheel,
'Twas the Devil that guided her way.

3.
She was just about five miles up in the Stretch
When a south-east gale began to blow.
They headed for shelter in Buccaneer Bay;
That's the only place there was to go.

4.
In Welcome Pass the mate was alert
For sight of the marker ahead,
But he cut 'er too short comin' out of the Pass,
And grounded on Tattenham Ledge.

5.
The barge dragged the tugboat off into the deep.
She sank twenty fathoms down.
Only the chief and the skipper survived;
The five other men were drowned.

6.
They salvaged the tugboat and she's workin' yet.
She has a new crew brave and bold,
But she'll never forget that cold Christmas Eve
Nor the ghosts of the five in her hold.

On Friday, December 11, 1953, at about 2 a.m., the seventy-five foot, wooden-hulled tug *C.P. Yorke* was proceeding up the coast from Vancouver to Menzies Bay, towing a barge loaded with four empty boxcars. Within an hour, the vessel was involved in a double accident which took the lives of five of the seven-member crew.

A gale warning had been issued by the weather office; but the actual winds over the waters between Sechelt and Pender Harbour were reported as blowing up to 35 m.p.h., a moderate gale, 7 on the Beaufort scale. A driving rain and the dark of a December night made visibility poor. The mate, Fred Crutchley, was at her wheel, and Capt. Roy Johnson was outside on deck helping guide the tug through the stormy blackness.

Stanly G. Triggs

The C.P. Yorke.

The vessel had passed Merry Island light and was just emerging from Welcome Pass into Malaspina Strait when she struck Collingham Reef, an underwater extension of South Thormanby Island. She settled quickly on the rocks with a heavy list. As the waters rushed over the deck, Capt. Johnson grabbed a life jacket, and got off a call for help on the radio, stating the tug "had gone aground at the entrance to Buccaneer Bay." The call was answered by the *Blackbird II*, which was close by.

In the ensuing confusion, the captain was swept overboard, leaving the crew clinging to the side of the leaning vessel. In the emergency, the chief engineer had handed the captain a flash-light to which he clung even after he sank into unconsciousness from exposure. Its light was later instrumental in saving his life.

Buccaneer Bay, to the west of the reef on which the *C.P. Yorke* was grounded, is formed by a depression between North and South Thormanby Islands. Its relatively shallow bottom of some 20 to 30 fathoms extends northward of the islands where it is known as Tattenham Ledge. Although the wind was strong and the seas churning, the six remaining crew members thought they stood a good chance of rescue by staying with the vessel. In any event, the lifeboat could not be launched safely. Since there seemed to be no great hurry, two of the crew may not have secured their life jackets thoroughly. It was while the crew waited that the second accident occurred. Just as unexpectedly as the tug had hit the reef, she was, according to her former owner, knocked off her perch and slid down some 20 fathoms to rest on Tattenham Ledge.

From this account, what had happened was a tragic coincidence. The barge which the tug had been towing was riding high in the water with its light load. Blown by the wind, it had, like a well-aimed billiard ball, struck the tug. Chief Engineer Bill McDonald was thrown into the water with the others, but luckily he came upon the tug's upturned lifeboat. He clung to it and was rescued some twenty hours later ten miles away on the shore of Nelson Island. He and the captain, who had been dramatically saved by the first mate of the tug *H & L* swimming with a life line, were the only survivors. Of the five who drowned, three bodies were recovered, one five miles away, and two were never found.

Two days after the accident the one-hundred-ton tug was raised by a salvage vessel. The *C.P. Yorke* had started her career in 1945 with the name *Kingcome*, given her as she came off the ways at Dollarton, B.C.

as a naval tug. She continued working until early in the 1970's when she was converted to a yacht with the name *Trojan*.

The song "The Wreck of the *C.P. Yorke*" was composed six years after the events by Stan Triggs, who for some time served as deckhand-cook on several west-coast tugs. Here is what he wrote of the ballad in 1961:

> This is a song that I made up when working on the tugboats. It is a true story about a real tugboat that went down off Tatenham (sic) Ledge one night just before Christmas 1954 (sic) sometime just after midnight. It is one of the best known marine disasters on the west coast and I would often hear the story repeated as we passed Tatenham (sic) Ledge. I knew I had to write a song about this. All that fall I could feel it building up inside. The tune came first, and I played it over and over on the mandolin, waiting for the words to follow. Then one stormy night near Christmas we were tied up in Long Bay waiting out the gale and the words came. I sang it for the crew the next day.
>
> (Stanley G. Triggs' notes to his Folkways Album # FG 3569, *Bunkhouse and Forecastle Songs of the Northwest*, New York, 1961)

Stan Triggs, it should be mentioned, was a genuine fo'c'sle singer. He wrote songs for his workmates and was later prevailed upon to record his music. The song should be heard or read with that in mind. A former owner of the *C.P. Yorke* recalled that the song had the story of the wreck "just about right." He also said that it was an unwritten law of the tugboat crews that the vessels are in port for Christmas. Mrs. Charles Cates, who worked on tugs herself for five years, tells of the tugs arriving in port always before Christmas Eve, each with a Christmas tree tied to the mast. The tug would not have been leaving port at that time. It would appear, from this information and from Stan Trigg's own note on the time of the wreck, that he had taken some licence for poetic effect with the precise time. Although the wreck actually occurred two weeks to the day before Christmas, the loss to the families and friends and the grim fact of the two bodies cast its pall over Christmas that year and, as evidenced by the song, over later Christmases as well. Another aspect of the ballad, perhaps also designed for effect, is its inclusion of the Devil and the "ghosts of the five in her hold." The author may have used these supernatural elements to express, from the confines of a tug, his feelings towards the lost fellow tugboat men and his attitude to "fate" itself. At the same time, he might have been aware that the supernatural appeared in traditional ballads from the British Isles, and intended the song to have a feeling of age and continuing tradition. How the crew members who first heard the song reacted to this aspect is not known. The song is sung in 1978 by numbers of people who enjoy folk songs. I do not know if it is sung on west coast tugs, but Stan Triggs' recording has sold many copies to a wide audience.

K.M. Papov

30

Kerry Papov of Nakusp, B.C., wrote this trucker's song.

The Truck Driver's Song

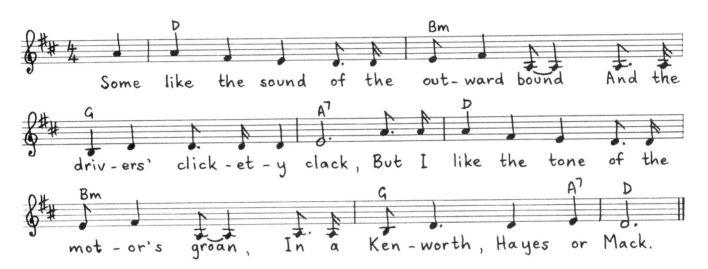

Some like the sound of the out-ward bound And the driv-ers' click-et-y clack, But I like the tone of the mot-or's groan, In a Ken-worth, Hayes or Mack.

1.
Some like the sound of the outward bound
And the driver's clickety-clack,
But I like the tone of the motor's groan,
In a Kenworth, Hayes, or Mack.

2.
My windshield shows me where I go,
And my mirrors where I've been.
My tandems roll and take their toll
Of the highways that I've seen.

3.
Well, I've learned to feel through the steering wheel
The road I cannot see,
And I hit the air 'cause I really care
For the rig that's under me.

4.
The rain beats down on the way so black,
And the night is blacker still.
I'll pull this load to the open road
On the far side of the hill.

5.
Now she's made of steel and nuts and bolts,
But you've got to treat her right,
Or the dizzy bitch will hit the ditch
And leave you cold and white.

6.
Now there's nothing left for me to say
That's not been said before,
So I'll just say as I go my way
That I like the diesel's roar.

"The Truck Driver's Song" reveals how one man thinks and feels
about truck driving. His personal view is so concretely and directly
stated that we not only share his experience but feel that it presents a
general truth about driving the great haulage trucks. The song tells
what it's like behind the wheel.

Kerry Papov of Nakusp on Upper Arrow Lake, who made the song a few years ago, has driven trucks in the Nakusp region for some twenty-five years. For many years he hauled logs to the mills from gypo logging operations. After the C.P.R. cut off steamship service on the Arrow Lakes (see song No. 27), he hauled waybill freight two hundred miles from Vernon over the rough roads of the Monashee Mountains. In recent years he has been carrying gravel for roadbuilding. Another job has been taking oil and heavy equipment to logging camps and mines. He has put most of the mileage on his two White trucks on the one-hundred-fifty miles of the region's single-lane gravel-topped back roads. The song brings the common element of all these jobs, the act of driving, to us with great immediacy.

Just as the whistle and rail sounds of trains stir the feelings of some people, Kerry tells us in his song that he is stirred by the sounds of the great haulage trucks. In the northwest, four makes of truck are prominent: Kenworth, Hayes, Mack and White, each of which carries with it an aura of engineered power, rugged strength and reliability. These vehicles have two wheels in front and four tandem pairs in a tandem assembly in the rear, making ten in all; a trailer adds another tandem with eight for a total of eighteen wheels. Loaded weights range from 23 to 27 tons (21,000 to 24,500 Kg.). The song puts you right in the cab of the rig, feeling through the steering wheel the road [you] cannot see," hitting the air brakes, facing the treacherous blackness of mountain roads on a rainy night—and if you make an error, "she" will make it fatal. What is meant by "the open road" is not specific—the term is relative. But "the highways that I've seen" suggests hauling on long runs over major paved roads. The song thus takes us beyond the back roads of the Nakusp area, but is rooted in Kerry Papov's immediate experience.

Kerry has played guitar since his teens. He plays flatpick with a Chet Atkins feel on a beautiful big Gibson, sings around home, and has more songs made and in the making.

Mack truck hauling in the southern interior, near Penticton, B.C.

B.C. Forest Service

Logs from the coastal rain forest,
Roberts Creek, B.C., 1938.

Hauling in the Interior, near
Kamloops.

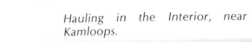

Logging & Sawmilling

31

Way Up The Ucletaw

Come all you bull-necked log-gers And hear me sing my
song, For it is ver-y short And it will not keep you
long. We had blan-kets for to trav-el, Bis-cuits for to
chaw. We were in search of pitch-backs Way up the Uc-let-aw.

1.
Come all you bull-necked loggers
And hear me sing my song,
For it is very short
And it will not keep you long.
Chorus
We had blankets for to travel,
Biscuits for to chaw.
We were in search of pitchbacks
Way up the Ucletaw.

2.
We're leaving Vancouver
With sorrow, grief and woe,
Heading up the country
A hundred miles or so.

3.
We hired fourteen loggers,
An we hired a man to saw.
We had a Chinee cook,
And he run the hotcakes raw.

The men in "Way Up the Ucletaw" are hand-loggers, men who turn standing trees into floating logs with only their own muscles as power and the rising tide as their giant helper. There were many such men at the turn of the century working on the shores of the Gulf of Georgia with its numerous islands, bays and inlets. They would select Douglas firs, the "pitchbacks" of the song, which could be felled directly onto a tidal beach or slid down a slope to salt water. With axes, saws, wedges, jacks and pulleys they bucked the trees into logs and readied them to be floated off at high tide. With a row boat, and often with a small sail, they would boom up their logs to await a tow to the mill.

These men were marginal operators, doing well when logs were in high demand; but they were the first to suffer when the market became glutted, as it did in the economic depression of the mid-1890's. The man from whom this song was collected told of a tent-town of workless hand-loggers on the north side of Vancouver's False Creek about 1896. It is likely that the "sorrow, grief and woe" reflects their common plight.

As logging has spread to the more remote parts of our coast, hand-loggers have continued to follow their beaver-like role, but in diminishing numbers. In a time of Forest Management Licences, Public Working Circles and a changed technology, the hand-logger with his pride, ingenuity and independence has almost disappeared.

With their muscles, simple tools, ingenuity and guts, the hand loggers helped maintain the early mills.

The "Ucletaw" refers to the Yuculta Rapids, the name given to a treacherous winding part of Seymour Narrows which is situated between Quadra and Sonora Islands. "Ucletaw" is spelt here as it sounds (yūk´-lě-taw) but is generally found as "Yuculta" on the maps, the name coming from the Indian people who lived thereabouts. Captain John T. Walbran (*British Columbia Coast Names*) gives "Eucluetaw" as an alternate name.

"Tooth picks" become a traveling billboard as timbers go east, while others are loaded on the square-riggers in the distance. Hastings Sawmills, c. 1900.

B.C. Provincial Archives

Buck's Camp Down At Monroe

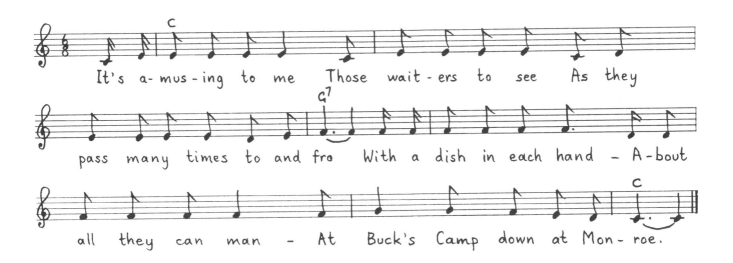

It's a-mus-ing to me Those wait-ers to see As they

pass many times to and fro With a dish in each hand — A-bout

all they can man — At Buck's Camp down at Mon-roe.

Author photo

1.
It's amusing to me
Those waiters to see
As they pass many times to and fro
With a dish in each hand—
About all they can man—
At Buck's camp down at Munroe.

2.
The locie does fine
As it makes the incline—
Makes it both puff, snort, and blow.
It would unman your nerves
As she slides round the curves
At Buck's Camp down at Monroe.

3.
McCormick is
Our foreman—
He's lazy as he's big;
He rolled a log
The other day
And killed our only pig.

Author photo

Rubber stamp of Vancouver local of Industrial Workers of the World showing date of incorporation. The Wobblies were largely responsible for improved conditions in the camps.

In the little song "Buck's Camp Down at Monroe," reportedly first heard on Vancouver Island about 1900, a logger ridicules the camp he came from—with its greenhouse flunkeys in the cookhouse, a railroad that promised a mishap, and a "gormless" foreman who carelessly ruined the only fresh pork. Buck's Camp in Monroe, Washington State, was hardly the singer's ideal. A brief look at the situation facing loggers at that time may help give the song more meaning.

Until the early years of this century, west coast loggers generally ate and slept near the giant trees they were felling. Hand loggers simply sheltered along the shore; but the men who produced the bulk of the logs lived in camps with a cookhouse and bunkhouses. The logging camp was part of a large scale organization and would be moved when distances for men, oxen or donkey engines became impractical. It was not until the logging railway and the motor truck came into use that a camp could become more permanent, the hub for logging over a wide area.

The men in these camps were industrial workers doing separate jobs in a larger process, and their life was consequently regimented. They rose at the shout of "It's daylight in the swamps!", ate communally in silence, and worked strenuously for long hours. With a work week of six days at ten hours a day, the loggers' life centered almost entirely on the job.

Living conditions in the early camps were rough, with crowded, ill-ventilated, murky sleeping quarters. There was inadequate provision for drying wet clothing in a rain-forest climate, and no facilities for bathing or for washing lice-infested clothing and blankets. Working such long hours, the men had little time for recreation, and no indoor space was provided. Even Sunday was primarily a time for personal chores, for patching and sewing clothing, shaving, haircutting, and make-shift washing. Camp operators found that men would tolerate much discomfort provided the food for which they paid was plentiful and varied. It became the mark of the west coast logger that he would work if he were well fed. Some loggers, sensing the crude limits of their lives, called themselves and their kind "timber beasts."

The loggers had one thing in common: nearly all had traveled across much of the continent working on job after job. Most of them had come from the plundered forests of New Brunswick, Maine, and the Great Lakes region, or as immigrants from Europe. Many had worked on railroad construction and had ended up in the logging camps. They were homeless men, who when they moved on carried their blankets and other belongings on their backs. These migrant workers, while prepared to sell their labor, tried to maintain a sense of their individual dignity and worth by exercising their right to withdraw that labor. When one of them had had enough of conditions in a camp, he would ask for his "time" (his pay), then roll up his blankets and leave. By selecting the camps in which they would work, the loggers exerted pressure on the operators to improve living and working conditions.

As a result of various pressures and through a policy of enlightened self-interest, camp managers who wished to attract and hold good workers made piece-meal improvements in conditions. Thus in the northwest around 1912 some camps installed baths and single steel bunks with mattresses. Such changes did not take place in an industrial vacuum. Working men had long believed that, if they joined together on matters of common interest, their just complaints and demands would be heeded, especially if they further agreed jointly to withdraw their labor unless enough improvements were forthcoming. The owners and managers of the logging and lumber companies fought against the men organizing themselves into such unions by firing and blacklisting any worker found giving the others leadership in that direction. He was branded a troublemaker, and if he persisted or seemed at all successful, the employers at times resorted to violence.

In the northwestern states and in western Canada the union which gained great support among general laborers was the Industrial Workers of the World, the I.W.W. In the years prior to World War I, the Wobblies, as I.W.W. members were popularly called, claimed 10,000 members in western Canada alone. But, while they effectively organized railway construction workers, they found the small and isolated logging camps with their high turnover of men too difficult. Nevertheless it was an I.W.W. strike in northwestern lumber camps in 1917 which won for the loggers blankets and sheets for their bunks and the eight-hour day. To celebrate this victory it is reported that the men made a bonfire of their old "bindles" (their blanket rolls). By 1920 these improved conditions were general in the northwest.

Marsh Underwood, a long time logger and foreman, gives this testimony in his book, *Log of a Logger*:

> "Wobblies" were considered radicals, but the improved conditions of camps were certainly brought about by these men, and credit should be given them.

The Wobblies always had songs, mostly parodies, to spread their ideas or, as they said on the cover of the *Little Red Song Book,* "to fan the flames of discontent." In 1921 this little remaking of "Old Folks At Home" was heard in a central Oregon camp:

> All up and down the Kootenay River*
> The bosses sadly roam.
> They cannot have their way for ever
> 'Cause we're making the camps like home.

* or Kootenai River, the U.S. name.
(There is more on the I.W.W. with Song No. 25)

"The lokey does fine..." Shawnigan Lake Lumber Co. No. 2, built in 1911, by Climax Locomotive Co., Cory, Pa. (c. 1914-15).

33

First stanza in a "stage Scandinavian accent":
   Ay ban Svensky fallin'-bucker
   And ay vork in de voods about two year
   And ay go down to Vancouver
   Yust to look at de Potlatch Fair.
Key:
   "I" sounds "ay"; "th" in *there* sounds "d"; "th" in *three* sounds "t"; initial "j" sounds "y"; "ee" in *been* shortens to "ben" or "ban."

The Potlatch Fair

I ben Swen-sky fal-lin'-buck-er And I work in the woods a-bout two years, And I go down to Van-cou-ver - Just to look on the Pot-latch Fair.

var. a)

1.
I ben Swensky fallin'-bucker
And I work in the woods about two years,
And I go down to Vancouver
Just to look at the Potlatch Fair.

2.
I got me a bottle of Campbell River,
And I jump on the boat 'bout half-past six;
There I meet three hundred loggers,
All going down to get teeth fixed.

3.
An' it's up to the "high-lead" just for fun,
And there I met one big fat girl.
She slapped me on the back and said,
"How d'ye do, Nels?"

4.
And I look around feelin' so funny,
I never see that girl before—
But I bein' foxy say, "Hello, Tilly,
Won't you come and have a drink?"

5.
We had a drink of "yicky yinger,"
Then we start into dance and sing,
And I tell all them Swensky fallers
That I'll pay for the whole darn thing.

6.
Then we drink some more gin and whisky
And I get up on a chair and say,
"Everybody make for jolly!
That's the style to make her pay."

7.
And I was a-ridin' out in a nice blue wagon
Up to the city judge to see.
The judge say, "Pay me fifty dollars, Ole;
You've been on an awful spree."

8.
And I paid the judge the fifty dollars—
All the money that I had.
For the Swensky faller it's no good luck,
And he's feeling mighty bad.

9.
I go down to the skid road
And I hired out there;
And I jumped the old *Cowichan* for Thurlow Island—
And to hell with the Potlatch Fair!

"The Potlatch Fair," dating from around 1920, need not really be a Swede's song for it was the common story of migratory loggers of the coastal northwest woods as they sought some pleasure on the "Skid Roads" of such large ports as Portland, Seattle and Vancouver. A "Skid Road" district, as found in these cities, originally was a real skid road over which teams of oxen pulled giant logs to a mill. As boats towed more logs to the mill, sailing ships carried the lumber produced across the oceans; and to serve the mill-workers, loggers and seamen, a general store, hotel and saloon soon appeared along the skid road. To these were added boarding houses, restaurants, shipping agents, ships' chandlers, hardware merchants, bawdy houses and hiring agencies. Given time, a favorable location and the addition of a railroad terminus, a few of these primitive skid road communities became parts of booming cities. Although the new business and cultural centers and residential districts grew apace, the skid road, where it all began, still catered to the single logger. In 1922 one logger, who had taken a long look at the skid road, tried to communicate his experience to other citizens who—perhaps living within a mile or so of the district—had probably never seen it from the gangplank of a coastal ship just in from the camps. He wrote:

> Have you ever thought of how we, the workers in the woods...
> are really approached and "entertained" when we visit our
> present centres of "civilization" and "culture"? What is the first
> thing we meet? The cheap lodging house, the dark and dirty
> restaurant, the saloon or the blind pig, the prostitutes operating
> in all the hotels, the moving picture and cheap vaudeville shows
> with their still cheaper, sensational programs, the freaks of all
> descriptions who operate on the street corners....

(Quoted in Jensen, *Lumber and Labor*, p. 107.)

Jeannie Moss photo

"...and I jump on the boat 'bout half-past six"—Princess Adelaide loading at Port McNeill, V.I., July 7, 1940.

B.C. Provincial Archives

"And I jumped the old Cowichan for Thurlow Island..." The Cowichan, built in Scotland in 1908, sank after a collision in heavy fog off Roberts Creek in 1925.

Slack time in a typical skid road bar. At the turn of the century, there were sixteen in the two blocks of Water Street between Cambie and Carral Streets, one of which was in the Grand Hotel. Note the new logger's boots.

The skid road was a social trap, a kind of invisible cage with well-displayed bait. The loggers, as transient workers many of whom were limited in their use of the English language, found it difficult to move beyond the environs of the skid road into regular city life. These vigorous men with their rolls of bills desperately sought release from the monotony and wretchedness of camp life; for a few days they caroused and consorted with the skid road women, perhaps felt they were the center of things for a few moments, but generally ended up broke, like the singer in "The Potlatch Fair."

"The Potlatch Fair," as the name of Vancouver's skid road scene, used the Chinook trade jargon word "potlatch." Its primary use is as the verb "to give"; as a noun it means simply "a gift," but it also denotes the ceremonial distribution of gifts as practised by all the Indian peoples of the northwest coast. In "The Potlatch Fair" it could have overtones of all these meanings, especially the last where a noted chief would give away his accumulated wealth to the point of impoverishing himself. Certainly the logger's spending was more like giving it away, and the skid road ritual demanded that he not stop till he ended up broke. Seattle businessmen for several years prior to World War I sponsored a week of festivities called "Potlatch Days." It is likely that this device for promoting civic awareness and sales, and having some fun at the same time, came to include the location of any binge, such as Vancouver's skid road.

In the remote up-coast logging camps, a logger could have difficulty getting his money to go to town. Much of the exchange was done on paper, his wages being balanced against his board bill and his spending at the camp commissary. To get the actual cash owing him or to get an advance if he were in debt to the company, he on occasion pleaded the "toothache," or, as one old timer called it, the "Irish toothache." The "toothache" also had a transferred meaning in the phrase "to get one's teeth fixed" which meant to go to town to find a woman.

Vancouver City Archives

34

The Grand Hotel

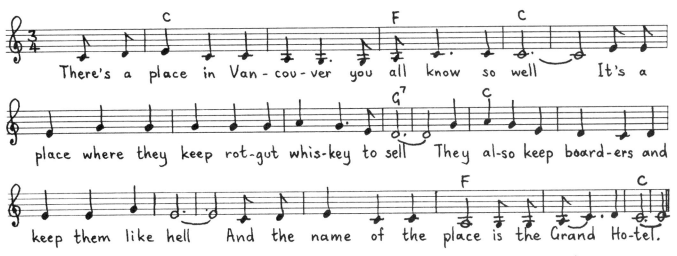

There's a place in Van-cou-ver you all know so well It's a
place where they keep rot-gut whis-key to sell They al-so keep board-ers and
keep them like hell And the name of the place is the Grand Ho-tel.

1.
There's a place in Vancouver you all know so well,
It's a place where they keep rot-gut whiskey to sell.
They also keep boarders, they keep them like hell,
And the name of that place is the Grand Hotel.

2.
In the Grand Hotel when the loggers come in,
It's amusing to see the proprietor grin.
He knows they've got money, he'll soon have it all;
"Come on, boys, have a drink!" you will hear Tommy
    call.

3.
Oh, the bartender laughs as the money rolls in;
They drink beer and whiskey, champagne, rum and gin,
Till they all get so boozy they can't drink no more,
And the loggers lay scattered all over the floor.

4.
In the morning the loggers wake up from their bed
Their money's all gone and, oh Lord, what a head!
They rush for the bar and call for a drink,
And Tommy gets busy a-slinging the ink:

5.
"Four bits* for your bed, though you slept on the floor,
And the breakfast you missed that will be four bits
    more;
And a four-dollar meal ticket, good at the bar,
And a pass back to camp on the old *Cassiar*."

*four bits—fifty cents

The Grand Hotel, 1929.

S.S. Cassiar

"The Grand Hotel" is a companion to "The Potlatch Fair," giving another view of the experience of loggers on Vancouver's skid road. In "The Potlatch Fair" a logger relates what happens to him when he goes from Campbell River to Vancouver for a spree. A day or so after arriving he is broke and disgusted, and hires out to a camp on Thurlow Island. As he boards the vessel for the trip up the coast, he curses the scene which deluded him and which he is glad to leave behind. In "The Grand Hotel" an amused observer records the way some other loggers encounter the same skid road.

The loggers in "The Grand Hotel" follow what is for them a customary pattern. They hit neither the highs nor the lows of the "Potlatch Fair" logger, but their stay is longer. They, nevertheless, are equally bent on achieving, through drinking and carousing, a release from the crushing monotony and deprivation of working a sixty-or-more-hour week for months in the coastal rain forest. Compared to the logger in "The Potlatch Fair," these loggers are on familiar and relatively secure territory; they know that their stay on the skid road will be costly, but that when it is over each will have the steamer ticket to return to his camp.

For years loggers knew the Grand Hotel would give them a special service. By placing their money in the care of the proprietor, Thomas J. Roberts—the "Tommy" of the song—they had the surety of a bed and their return passage. All a logger had to do was give Roberts his roll of bills and ask to be told when it was spent. Tommy's concern was by no means disinterested, but at least the skid road visitor would not be the victim of direct theft. When Tommy got "busy a-slingin' the ink," i.e. totting the bill, he knew his holiday was over.

Tommy Roberts came to the skid road soon after he migrated to Vancouver from New Brunswick in 1888, when he was just fifteen years of age. He shortly became a partner in a skid road business and in a few years took over the Granville Hotel, which he renamed the Grand Hotel. He has been portrayed as an open-handed and generous man, ready to take a chance in any kind of business enterprise. His muscular physique contributed to a swashbuckling presence. An informant recalled his black mustache and jaunty fedora. He also wore a solitaire diamond ring which figured in his death at the age of forty-five.

In 1918 a holdup occurred at a regular twice-a-week poker game which he and other invited participants attended in a West End house. When the robber told Roberts to remove the solitaire, Tommy said he could not get it off and presenting his hand, said, "Here, take it off yourself, if you want it so bad." As the gunman tugged at the ring, Roberts was pulled towards him. He leaped at the robber, and in the struggle which followed was shot in the head, falling instantly. His wife continued to run the hotel for a few years, but there is no record that the custom at the Grand Hotel of managing the loggers' affairs survived.

"When the pond is full of timber,…"   Public Archives of Canada

35

The Greenchain Song

You who live a life of leis-ure, you who live a life of ease, In your man-sions in the count-ry or your yacht up-on the seas, Does your con-science ev-er pic-ture on the tab-let of your brain The sad thought of men in miser-y, pul-lin' lum-ber off the chain?

1.
You who live a life of leisure, you who live a life of ease,
In your mansions in the country, on your yacht upon the seas,
Does your conscience ever picture on the tablet of your brain
The sad thought of men in misery, pullin' lumber off the chain?

2.
When the pond is full of timber, the jack ladders running wild,
And the sawyer in his carriage has the bandsaw set and filed,
From the headrig to the trimsaw through the planer moves the chain
Of that endless pile of lumber out upon that long greenchain.

3.
Now, the pondmen think they're Bunyans, and the scaler thinks he's God,
And the sawyer thinks that each of them's a lazy, useless sod.
But if the truth were ever looked for in the lies that pour like rain,
You would find out that the heroes are the workers on the chain.

4.
When the shift-boss hits that button, then you'd better look alive
'Cause the lumber comes a-rolling like the bees out of a hive,
And you'll feel that sweat come pouring as each muscle screams with pain,
And you'll wonder if it's worth it, working on the long greenchain.

5.
See the grader eye the lumber as it moves along the chain;
With his keel he makes the grading, marks it down for knot and grain:
These salutes to profiteering we treat with complete disdain,
For what's it mean to we who toil out on that long greenchain?

6.
When I go to meet my Maker, there is just one hope I hold,
That St. Peter at the Golden Gate won't leave me in the cold;
But if he sends me down below, this truth to you I'll tell:
I still won't be unhappy, 'cause that greenchain's worse than hell!

Sawmilling is inseparable from the history of settlement in British Columbia. The first mill was at work in 1848, one year before Vancouver Island became a Crown colony. By 1916 there were some four hundred mills reported to be operating in the province, and in the early 1970's the average number actually running had about doubled. The cut of the mills today is over ten billion board feet, compared with a little over one billion sixty years ago. Today the annual capacity of just one of the province's giant modern mills (some 230 million board feet) equals the total lumber sawn in 1901 by all the medium and large mills. These 1901 mills included the one at Chemainus on Vancouver Island and the Hastings and Moodyville mills on Burrard Inlet, all well-known for the cargoes of lumber they exported aboard sailing ships to Australia, China and Japan, and Great Britain. Japan and Great Britain are still major importers of our lumber, but the United States and the continental part of the European Common Market now take more.

The productive capacity of the great modern mills, such as those at Chemainus and Alberni, is the result of well over a century of developing technology. Changes have taken place in saw designs, energy sources, and transportation methods within the mill. The mills first used straight, then circular saws; next came straight saws grouped into gangs, followed by thin and less wasteful band saws, which were ultimately arranged in groups of opposing pairs. Power came first from the water wheel, then the steam engine, the internal combustion engine, and the electric motor. The early mills used the harnessed energy only to run the saw; once plants were of sufficient size, the power was applied to move the log into the mill, along the production line, and out the other end as freshly cut or green lumber.

When a log enters a mill, the first cutting device to engage its round end is called the "head rig." Until 1962 the head rig was always a saw, but in that year an invention called a "head chipper" was first used to square the log, which then was conveyed to the saws. The chipper processes in one step a part of the tree that was formerly wasted. The squared timber is then placed on a carriage to be fed to the saws. Large mills have a number of production lines, enabling boards with a variety of dimensions to be cut without continually shutting down to readjust the saws. Each of these developments in sawmilling technology promoted a greater efficiency, which could be turned to higher profits and to competitive advantage.

Most steps in the large mills have now been automated to a high degree. The last phase in the process is the handling of the boards as they stream off the production line or lines. The lumber must be separated by grade and sized into piles ready for removal. Taking its name from the conveyor chains which carry the green lumber, this part of the mill is called the "greenchain." In a few mills, it is now at least partially automated.

Of all the workers in a sawmill, the one who likes his job least is the man on the greenchain, for work on the greenchain is the most arduous in the mill. Relentlessly the conveyor produces the boards which must be removed as fast as they appear. The pace and the lifting are backbreaking. Larger boards, however awkward, must be carried single-handed to their appropriate piles.

The greenchain is the usual introduction to working in a sawmill. The work requires no special skill, pays the minimum wage, and has the lowest status of all the jobs. If a person stays on the greenchain a long time, he at least proves he has endurance, but he may be accused of being all brawn and no brain. If he is determined to work in a better job, he may still have to stay a year or so on the greenchain before he gets a chance at a skilled job. Some occupations require long experience and special training as well as aptitude, such as those of sawyer, scaler and grader. Other jobs, such as that of a pondman, entail less drudgery and offer a more interesting environment, but are more dangerous. The greenchain worker is well aware of his lowly position and in defence declares himself the real hero because of the physical endurance he must display.

The infamy of the greenchain as a place to work is widely known. The singer in "The Greenchain Song" gives vent to his feelings in the last line when he declares that the "long greenchain" is "worse than hell." The song is not just a complaint; it is a literate rendering of a howl of resentment, anger and pain. Even those men who have done the job for a long time and are apparently physically strong break down in time with back, shoulder and arm trouble. But most of the bad reputation comes from the painful experiences of men who are not in good condition. Their bodies are soon wracked with symptoms of strain and may suffer serious damage. If not fired because they are obviously unable to do the work, they either book off sick or quit. Their recollections, along with those of the older employee whose body finally gives under the stress of trying to keep pace with the conveyor chain, have made greenchain work synonymous with the worst of industrial slavery.

The Woodworker

"Pullin' lumber off the chain"—the end of the milling process.

Mining: Prospecting, Coal & Hard Rock Mines

36

Way Up In The Monashee Range

There's a strike at Mis-ty Moon Lake, And I'm set and read-y to go; For there's ground that a fel-low can stake, But it's cov-ered at pres-ent with snow — Way up in the Mon-a-shee Range.

1.
There's a strike at Misty Moon Lake,
And I'm set and ready to go;
For there's ground that a fellow can stake,
But it's covered at present with snow—
Way up in the Monashee Range.

2.
So we'll wait till the hills get green,
Then we're off to hit the trail,
For we want to see what's to be seen,
Whether we strike it rich or we fail—
Way up in the Monashee Range.

3.
It's a long way off from the road,
And the climb's a hard one to make,
But my feet itch to pack a load
On the trail to Misty Moon Lake—
Way up in the Monashee Range.

Author photo

An anonymous prospector with his pack animal—one of the thousands who panned for color and sought the mother lode in the Cordilleras following the early gold rushes.

The man with a blanket roll, pick and gold pan who came searching for new showings of placer gold in the banks and bed of the lower Fraser River in 1858 called himself a "prospector." The terms "prospector" and "prospecting" had been coined a few years earlier in California. But by the 1880's a new image was developing: the prospector, toting a back pack, now climbs about the rocky terrain picking and hammering at rocks he suspects contain metals. He at first looks for lode gold, gold held in quartz, but soon finds that his discoveries of silver, lead, zinc and copper ores are also of value. He develops a geologist's eye for the folded, upthrust, faulted and eroded rock over which he walks. He occasionally uses a pan but more often a knife and magnifying glass.

This new breed of prospector made the discoveries which resulted in the mining boom of the 1890's and early years of this century in the Boundary and Kootenay Districts, a boom built upon heavily capitalized mines which produced not only ore but cities, railroads, paddlewheelers, sawmills, and a bustling complex of communities. From 1890 to 1910 prospectors, seeing such wealth and sharing in it, if only very rarely making a fortune themselves, scraped and chipped at every rock out-cropping in southern British Columbia from the Rockies to the Pacific. Over the years a statistically demonstrated truism arose amongst mining people that it took one thousand showings or discoveries of metallic mineralization to produce one mine. Despite the odds, prospecting was the trusted method of exploration supported by promoters and capitalists, but for many prospectors it became a way of life.

The man who made "Way Up in the Monashee Range" caught the prospector's fever early in the century and years later realized the prospector's dream by having one of his claims become a mine. Prospectors have continued to enter the field drawn by that age-old fantasy—the pot of gold at the end of the rainbow. In the 1930's, ten thousand information guides to geology for prospectors were printed by the British Columbia government's Department of Mines, first in pamphlet, then in booklet form. Who so eagerly took those thousands of booklets? Some would have gone to the simply curious. But many would have been sought out by men who in their daily work clambered over mountainous land, men such as miners, loggers, surveyors, ranchers, railway workers, even fishermen, who would climb up from the seashore and scratch and chip at the rocks. Another group were the otherwise unemployed men during the Depression of the 1930's who tried to eke out a living by mining placer gold, often reworking old claims. The price of gold had risen, especially after Great Britain went off the Gold Standard in 1931, until it was fixed at $35 per ounce by the United States in 1934. This last group were trying desperately to survive in the only way they knew how; they continued to preach the gospel of individual initiative, self-reliance and material success at a time when many others of their class were beginning to question the very foundations of the economic system.

During 1973 there were some 2,000 prospectors at work in British Columbia. Instead of traveling by canoe or pack horse, they now use the motorcycle, jeep, plane or helicopter, perhaps all four. About half of them are direct descendants of the men who made the first base metal discoveries in this region.

The Brechin Mine, Nanaimo, c. 1900.   B.C. Provincial Archives

37

Are You From Bevan?

Hel-lo, stran-ger, how do you do? There's some-thing I'd like to say to you.

You seem sur-prised I re-cog-nize; I'm no com-pan-y stool but I just sur-mise

You're from the place I'm long-ing to be. Your smil-ing face seems to say to me

You're from the is-land, Your land and my land, So tell me can it be —

Chorus:
Are you from Bev-an? I said from Bev-an Where those fields of stumps they

beck-on to me. I'm glad to see you! Tell me how be you, And those

friends I'm long-ing to see? If you're from U-nion Bay or Courte-nay or

Cum-ber-land An-y place be-low that Be-van sec-ond dam Are you from Bev-an? I said from Bev-an, 'Cause I'm from Bev-an too!

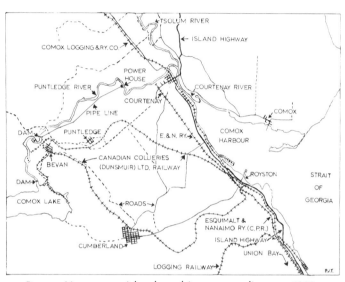

Bevan, Vancouver Island, and its surroundings, c. 1920.

1.
Hello, stranger, how do you do?
There's something I'd like to say to you.
You seem surprised I recognize;
I'm no company stool but I just surmise
You're from the place I'm longing to be.
Your smiling face seems to say to me
You're from the island, your land and my land,
So tell me can it be—

Chorus
Are you from Bevan? I said from Bevan
Where those fields of stumps they beckon to me.
I'm glad to see you!
Tell me how be you,
And those friends I'm longing to see?
If you're from Union Bay or Courtenay or Cumberland
Any place below that Bevan second dam—
Are you from Bevan? I said from Bevan,
'Cause I'm from Bevan too!

2.
It was way back in 19 and 12
Our gas committee was put on the shelf.
First we walked out, then we were locked out—
Then by a foul we were all but knocked out.
Our union miners faced guns and jail,
Hundreds of us were held without bail,
But by August 1914 our labor they were courting,
But they blacklisted me—

"Are You From Bevan?" is a mixture of nostalgia and grim recollection. The song tells in brief the story of a two-year episode in the long struggle of the coal miners of Vancouver Island to have the major mine owners accept their right to form a union. In the song a man—no longer a coal miner on the island—hails another whom he remembers from one of the colliery communities in the Cumberland area. He recalls the incident which precipitated the two-year dispute, the firing and blacklisting of the miner's representative on a Gas Committee at one of the Dominion Collieries' mines. He then tells of the men's reaction at Cumberland in September, 1912, where the blacklisted miner had sought work only to be turned away by the management. The men took a joint "holiday" to protest this discrimination and to discuss what further they should do. The next day the management ordered them to take their tools from the mine unless they would sign individual two-year contracts. The song then refers to the "foul" that nearly knocked them out. The "foul" was collusion in strikebreaking activities between the provincial government of McBride and Bowser and the owners of Canadian Collieries (Dunsmuir) Ltd. The strikebreaking included: employment in Cumberland of men, mostly Chinese, whom the employers were able to intimidate; turning a mine and its townsite into an armed camp with special police and eventually with militia; condoning of armed strikebreakers at Extension, near Nanaimo, when there was no evidence to suggest that the strikers were armed or intending to arm themselves; arrest by duplicity of men gathered in Nanaimo in peaceful assembly; and finally maintaining military rule over the entire mining area to ensure that no union organization could possibly succeed.

A main concern of the workers was for conditions of safety in the Vancouver Island mines. Mining coal underground is for a number of natural reasons hazardous even in the best conditions, but the record on the island had been very poor. In 1884, 23 men were killed; in 1887 at Nanaimo 148 men; in 1889 at Wellington 75 men; in 1901 at Extension 17 men; in 1909 at Extension 33 men. This incomplete list shows that to the miners of 1912 the threat of gas explosions and fire was vividly present. Accidents with blasting, falling rock and moving machinery in 1912 in the Canadian Collieries' mines resulted in 2.12 deaths per 1000 workers per year.

Arguments for a union ranged from those based on concepts of human rights and dignity to those dealing with wages, working conditions and safety. Mine owners like the Dunsmuirs had amassed fortunes and wanted no interference after decades of profitable management. As a means of keeping money costs down and frustrating the demands of the men, the owners had used many types of discrimination including tying wage differences to racial differences; they fought against the eight-hour day, and when it became law they obstructed its implementation; they readily took the gamble when mine safety was marginal. When laws were passed to make the miners' work less dangerous, the miners welcomed government concern, but they believed that these safety regulations could be effective only if the men had the protection of their own union.

On Vancouver Island in 1912 the four coal mine companies employed 3,500 men. Canadian Collieries (Dunsmuir) Ltd., bought two years earlier by the railway promoters Mackenzie and Mann, pursued the anti-union policies of the former Dunsmuir owners. The other three companies, although operating "company unions," supported the Canadian Collieries' opposition to bona fide unions. After the United Mine Workers of America had received repeated invitations from a substantial number of Vancouver Island miners, the union in 1911 sent organizers to the island. The miners from the Cumberland, Nanaimo and Ladysmith areas believed that only the backing of a large union would overcome the adamant opposition of the coal owners. The dispute in September, 1912 over the blacklisting of one man quickly became an issue of union recognition. After being locked out by Canadian Collieries for seven months, the men and their union organizers brought the miners of the other three companies out on strike for union recognition. This occurred on May 1, 1913, but they did not know at that time how far the owners' resistance would go. As summer approached, numerous efforts were made to get the two sides together. In June, the Vancouver Board of Trade's offer to mediate was rebuffed by the big coal mine operators who said that there was "nothing to arbitrate"!

In mid-August a riot occurred on the Canadian Collieries' property at Extension, apparently sparked by a rumor that the strikebreakers had shot six striking miners. In the ensuing turmoil company houses and mine buildings were burned, a store was looted and the strike-breakers were driven from the site. This proved disastrous for the union. Attorney-General William Bowser sent the militia to the coal areas, men were arrested, and the mines were kept operating with strikebreakers until a year later when agreements were signed with miners' committees in the separate mines. One coal mine company was an exception, the smallest of the four. After the strike had run three months they agreed to an arbitrator; ironically an agreement was concluded on the day of the Extension riot. That company signed a union contract with its employees later in August. The U.M.W.A. paid strike money to striking miners whether or not union members until June, 1914. At $16,500 per week, they supported the men to a total of $1,500,000. After nearly two years the struggle was given up, and the mines returned to regular operation. Many of the miners were blacklisted and never worked again on Vancouver Island. For years there was a legacy of bitterness. But the solidarity of the miners in a just cause and their commonly-shared hardships did allow them to look back in pride. One veteran of the strike quoted the old

"...those fields of stumps..." at Dunsmuir's Canadian Colliery Company town, Cumberland, in 1889.

Safety was high in the miners' concerns. Coal owners used various pressures to coerce the men to take chances when conditions in the mine were not patently dangerous yet did not clearly meet the miners' safety standards. Public opinion and government response eventually forced a more responsible attitude. The picture shows a rescue team from Fernie, B.C. at the International Contest in Nanaimo, September 1, 1919.

aphorism: "No strike is wholly lost," for, as he explained, most of the miners' specific demands regarding working conditions were met by August, 1913. Further, the publicity of the workers' cause made way for the general acceptance of the right of workers to organize with a union of their own choice.

Bevan in the song became a symbolic location of the 1912-14 dispute. It was a particularly suitable choice, for everything in Bevan was owned by the Mackenzie and Mann interests—"the land, coal, houses, store, hotel, even the road leading to the mine"; and since Bevan was out of the general public's eye, the union supporters there felt quickly the full force of the owners' anti-union tactics. Not only would the company management not meet with the men, but families were evicted from their homes. One man remembers his mother standing outside their house with her apron full of rocks for his father to throw at the scabs or blacklegs, who were trying to move into locked-out miners' houses. The McBride-Bowser government ignored appeals by the miners for aid in negotiations with the mine owners; instead they sent special police. In the Cumberland area by late August, 1913, there was a government force of 20 to 30 mounted police, 100 or more special police, and over 300 soldiers with arms and a field gun.

After Mackenzie and Mann took over the Dunsmuir collieries in 1910, the stated capital of the company increased overnight from two to fifteen million dollars. These railway promoters became coal mine promoters with visions of their own coal fueling their railways and a projected global shipping line. They sold shares in their new coal company on the London money market to a reported total capitalization of $25,000,000. Some of this fresh money was invested in the Bevan mines with a new railway spur, a new townsite, a second dam on the Puntledge River, and a powerhouse for the electrification of the mining operation. It has been plausibly suggested that the two notorious promoters were pleased that they could use the dispute with the workers as an excuse for not paying dividends on these recent shares. They wished to sustain their reputations in London where they were again selling government-backed bonds for their Canadian Northern Railway, then being built on the mainland.

38

Bowser's Seventy-Twa

Oh, did you see the kilt-ies, boys? The laugh would near-ly
kilt you, boys, The day they came to kill both great and small. With
bay-on-et shot and shell To blow you all to hell, Did
Bow-ser with his gal-lant Sev-en-ty-Twa. Then hur-
rah, boys, hur-rah, for Bow-ser's Sev-en-ty-Twa! The han-dy, can-dy,
dan-dy Sev-en-ty-Twa! 'Twill make the world look small Run
on by Colon-el Hall And Bow-ser with his gal-lant Sev-en-ty-Twa.

Hall. Hur-rah, boys, hur-rah, for Bow-ser's Sev-en-ty-Twa.

1.
Oh did you see the kilties, boys?
The laugh would nearly kilt you, boys,
The day they came to kill both great and small.
With bayonet, shot and shell,
To blow you all to hell,
Did Bowser with his gallant Seventy-Twa.
Chorus
Then hurrah, boys, hurrah,
For Bowser's Seventy-Twa!
The handy, candy, dandy Seventy-Twa!
'Twill make the world look small
Run on by Colonel Hall
And Bowser with his gallant Seventy-Twa.

2.
They stood some curious shapes, these boys,
They must have sprung from apes, these boys,
Dressed up in kilts to represent the law.
Ma conscience, it was grand,
Hurrah for old Scotland,
And Bowser with his gallant Seventy-Twa!

3.
They could not stand at ease, these boys;
They had no strength, believe me, boys;
Some had to stand upon their guns or fall.
And many a mother's son
Had never seen a gun,
But mind you, they were Bowser's Seventy-Twa!

4.
It beat the band to see them land
And make that grand heroic stand,
The emblem of the government and the law.
And we'll not forget the day
They stormed Departure Bay,
Did Bowser and his gallant Seventy-Twa.

Last Chorus
Then hurrah, boys, hurrah,
For Bowser's Seventy-Twa!
The handy, candy, dandy Seventy-Twa!
'Twill make the world look small
Run on by Colonel Hall—
Hurrah, boys, hurrah, for Bowser's Seventy-Twa!

"Bowser's Seventy Twa" is a document in song from the late summer of 1913 when the people of Nanaimo and other coal mining communities on Vancouver Island were put under military rule. It is evidence of the climate of opinion in those communities after thousands of miners, their wives and families had been subjected to an eleven-month lock-out compounded by a four-month strike. From the beginning of the lock-out the miners had appealed to the provincial government to support its own laws regarding safety in the coal mines, and had met with silence. The government, asked to support basic human and economic rights, reacted only when property rights were violated. And then their action was to dispatch armed militia and make wholesale arrests. While the Attorney-General thundered about keeping law and order, his actions effectively sustained the past privileges of the big coal mine owners and made the law and authority of British Columbia a mockery. Thus, when the government introduced military rule into a basically non-violent situation, the miners and their wives met the uniforms and machine guns with quiet scorn. "Bowser's Seventy Twa" cloaks outrage and bitterness in satirical verse. Such was the repression of those August days that one of the men credited with making the song, Bill Willis, was arrested for singing it.

On the evening following the August 13 rioting at Extension, Acting Premier and Attorney-General W.J. Bowser ordered militia units from Victoria and Vancouver to the island coal-mining areas. Lt. Col. A.J. Hall, in command of the whole Civil Aid Force (as it was officially known), arrived personally with the Victoria force (which was composed of over four hundred troops) at Departure Bay near Nanaimo at 7:30 a.m. on the 14th. Meanwhile the Vancouver force (some three hundred strong, including the 72nd Seaforth High-

*"'Twill make the world look small
Run on by Colonel Hall..."*

B.C. Provincial Archives

Top
When union miners in Nanaimo organized a special demonstration for May 1, 1914, the British "Labour Day," a group of B.C. Mounted Police was dispatched from Oakalla.

Center
"Bowser's Seventy-Twa"—the 72nd Seaforth Highlanders, whose name was joined to Attorney General Bowser's to make the satirical tag for the "Civil Aid Force."

Bottom Left
Police and soldiers escorting some of the 256 miners arrested.

Bottom Right
After an eleven month lock-out and strike with scabs taking their jobs and homes, union miners clashed with strike-breakers by the Extension mine, south of Nanaimo. One bystander received gunshot wounds and considerable company property was damaged. In the debris of the burnt mine entrance, this picture shows ruined motors used for hauling coal cars.

B.C. Provincial Archives

B.C. Provincial Archives

B.C. Provincial Archives

landers) had landed at Union Bay en route to Cumberland. Some fifty of the Highlanders arrived two days later at Departure Bay; they camped conspicuously at the Nanaimo wharf.

Martial law was never declared, but military control was effective. Col. Hall set up control of movement and assembly and instituted surveillance and censorship of telephone, telegraph and press communications. He had banned a miners' meeting on August 15, and when on the 18th he allowed such a meeting, (called to discuss the union agreement with the Vancouver and Nanaimo Coal Company) he did so for a purpose. "At 8:00," wrote the Rev. John N. Hedley in the *The Labour Trouble in Nanaimo District,*

> it was announced that soldiers were surrounding the building. At 9:00 the colonel in command asked for the chairman. Upon going outside he was shown the soldiers on every side of the building and a machine gun in the rear. On his return he informed the men that they had been commanded to begin leaving the hall in two minutes in single file, and any man running would be instantly shot or bayoneted.

In this naked display of force, the 72nd were in the forefront; they also acted later as guards when the miners were taken from the jail to the court and back again. Small wonder they were singled out for satire in cartoon and song as "Bowser's Seventy Twa."

Arrests including labor and political leaders eventually numbered over 250. Aside from injuries to pride caused by taunts and comments such as are in this song, the volunteer soldiers suffered no battle scars. While the militiaman's first impression was that they would be on duty for about a week, Bowser soon announced that they would be there for some months. Despite continuing criticism that the government was supporting the anti-union policies of Mackenzie and Mann and the other big operators, Bowser kept the Civil Aid Force, including fifty of the "Seventy Twa" on Vancouver Island until August 15, 1914, after the outbreak of World War I.

"Bowser's Seventy Twa" is but one of many songs which built and maintained morale both before and after the mid-August riots. Before and after their arrests the miners used the "Marseillaise" as a marching song. We have only the titles of two other songs used: "Strikers' Rally" and "Drive the Scabs Away." Judge Howay, whose harsh sentences caused much bitterness, denounced the miners' wives for singing such songs. That the arrested miners were denied bail is reflected in this short song still remembered in 1962:

> Nanaimo jail, Nanaimo jail,
> Full of good union men!
> They are good men, they are true men,
> Fighting for the U.M.W. of A.

Another short rallying song made by a jailed miner forecast the fall of the Bowser government in the election of 1916:

> Run Bowser, run! We will beat you at the poll!
> Run, Bowser, run! We will beat you to your hole!
> You thought you could break our spirit
> But you have only hastened the day
> When we will make the companies recognize the U.M.W.A.

39

Hard Rock Miner

A group of miners at the Le Roi Mine, Rossland, B.C., c. 1900. Note candles, soft hats and dinner pails.

B.C. Provincial Archives

I met you in a quartz mine in that good old town of Butte. You cer-tain-ly looked cute, dressed in that muck-er's suit; And the shif-ter said, "Come on, boys, get the muck in-to the chute, Then I'll show you how to run that big ma-chine!" But times have changed since then, old pal, I've been pro-mot-ed since; The po-si-tion that I hold to-day would el-e-vate a prince — For I'm a hard rock min-er, I run the wat-er Ley-ner down in the dust and dirt You'll see me ev-ery even-ing, when the

140

Kim-ber-ley lights are gleam-in' Wring-ing sweat out of my shirt.

Three years in the Flin-Flon, and four in the Yuk-on, Two in the Coeur D'Al-ene, But

you lost me, part-ner, when you went to the Co-balt And I to the South Lor-rain. Hol-y

gee, but I'm tired, I wish that I'd get fired, I'd go where the green grass

grows, Well I know that I'd be pin-in' to get back to min-in' Up where old Mark Creek flows.

I met you in a quartz mine in that good old town of
      Butte,
You certainly looked cute, dressed in that mucker's suit,
And the shifter said, "Come on, boys!
Get the muck into the chute,
Then I'll show you how to run that big machine!"
But times have changed since then, old pal,
I've been promoted since;
The position that I hold today would elevate a prince—

1.
For I'm a hard rock miner, I run the water Leyner,
Down in the dust and dirt.
You'll see me every evening when the Kimberley lights
      are gleamin'
Wringing sweat out of my shirt:

2.
Three years in the Flin-Flon, and four in the Yukon,
Two in the Coeur d'Alene,
But you lost me, partner, when you went to the Cobalt
And I to the South Lorrain:

3.
Holy gee, but I'm tired, I wish that I'd get fired,
I'd go where the green grass grows,
Well, I know that I'd be pinin' to get back to minin'
Up where old Mark Creek flows.

Bar-and-arm mounted drill at Le Roi Mine, c. 1900. The single hose to the machine indicates it is a "widow-maker."

Hard rock mining, also called lode mining, usually entails a three-part sequence: (1) breaking the rock (drilling and blasting), (2) loading (mucking), and (3) transporting (hauling and hoisting). Since prehistoric times, most mining around the world has followed this pattern. Changes occurred within the cycle as methods of working with metals and breaking rock improved and as the use of power-driven machinery increased.

Today large-scale lode mines and giant open-pit operations display a high degree of mechanization, but at the beginning of hard rock mining in British Columbia in the mid-1880's, conditions were relatively primitive. Compressed-air hammer drills, invented in 1855 and improved over some thirty years, were available. However, in small operations and for certain tasks, it was still common to find a man or a pair of men making blasting holes with a hammer and steel-rod drill, a process called "single-jacking" or "double-jacking." Invention of two types of dynamite in the 1860's revolutionized blasting, which for two hundred years had been done with gunpowder. The new explosives also were improved by the time hard rock mining began in the province.

The method of clearing away the ore and waste rock from a blasted rock face was the last part of the procedure to be improved. Picking and shovelling the muck, as the broken rock is called, into a wheelbarrow or, more generally, into an ore car remained relatively unchanged until the 1930's when mechanical scrapers and mucking machines were introduced. In the 1970's, there is, of course, still much pick-and-shovel work in mines. Without mechanization, muckers often work as a team rotating their three basic tasks — picking loose rock off the road and wall and breaking oversize pieces; shovelling muck into the ore car; and pushing the loaded car to the dump, a job called "tramming." By 1905, the self-dumping ore car was invented; a trammer could then mechanically empty the muck down a chute, one of the vertical passages or "raises" joining the mine's horizontal passages or "levels." The chute led to a lower level where the muck would land in a larger ore car. A train of such cars would then be hauled to the mine shaft to be hoisted out of the mine in an elevator-like cage.

A few names found in the songs may need explaining. The "shaft house" in "Taku Miners" is the housing over the shaft, the vertically driven access to the mine. Two kinds of pneumatic drills are mentioned in "I'm Only a Broken-down Mucker." A horizontal tunnel is a "drift," and a "drifting machine" is a pneumatic hammer-drill designed for drilling horizontally. An ore-bearing

Cont.

Hard rock miners have a reputation for working hard and playing hard. After a period in a remote mining operation with little recreation, a miner would commonly head for the bright lights of the city. Even more to type, two miners who had teamed up on the job would go to town together and there, based in one of the hotels frequented by miners, spend their rolls of money on a prolonged binge. The miners have shared with loggers and sailors (and in Australia, shearers) this cycle of confined work and release. For the miners it is especially important to have a buddy, not only for companionship but also for safety. When the two partners hired themselves out again, if the mine they had come from had a good safety record and if supervision and living conditions suited them, they might try to hire on again. But being broke and footloose, they could readily hire out to another mine providing they were both taken on. With this mobility and the cyclic work pattern, a pair of miners over a few years could travel the breadth of the country. Even married men moved around from one remote camp to another. In some places in British Columbia like Kimberley or Britannia where there was a huge ore body, a townsite grew up around the mine allowing miners to settle down. Technological changes have made mining processes more efficient, and since the 1940's union organization has given miners a place in determining conditions of employment and safety. Nevertheless the old patterns of mobility dating back to the early years of the century remain.

The domain of these miners is the three metal-bearing regions of Canada: the Cordilleran region, the Canadian Shield and, to a lesser degree, the Appalachian region of the Maritimes. The metal mines of the Shield are found in a broad arc encircling Hudson Bay reaching from Quebec through Ontario and Manitoba to the Northwest Territories. In the west the Cordilleras pass from Alaska through the Yukon Territory and British Columbia south to Mexico. Historically the mining industry of southeast British Columbia was an extension of the mining activity in Montana and Idaho. From the early 1890's for many years western miners worked back and forth across the Canada-United States border.

The mines, districts or towns listed in the variant texts of this song are evidence of the migratory habits of the miners. Malartic is in northwest Quebec. Cobalt, South Lorrain and "Northland" (Kirkland Lake) are in north Ontario. Geraldton is in northwest Ontario; Flin Flon in Manitoba; and Yellowknife on Great Slave Lake. In British Columbia were Kimberley, Stewart, and Wells ("Cariboo Gold"). The "Yukon" could refer to any one of a number of lode gold mines in the Territory. The "Coeur d'Alene" mine is in Wallace, Idaho. The mines mentioned broadly date the song, since they were all open at some time between the mid-1920's and 1950.

142

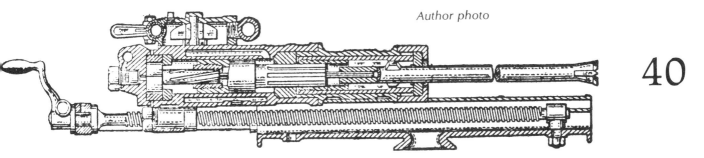

Author photo

"Leyner-Ingersoll" mounted hammer drill.

40

Taku Miners

1.
We are miners, Taku miners,
To the shaft house we must go.
With our oil bottles on our shoulders
We are marching to and fro.

2.
On the line, boys; on the line, boys.
Catch the cage and stand in line,
Till the shifter comes and tells you,
"You must drill her off on time."

Chorus
Loose the swing and jack the bar.
Come in on the arm; you're out too far.
Way up to the dump and we call her a hole—
A son-of-a-gun, this mining for gold!

3.
Watch that light, boys! Watch that light, boys!
The mine captain's in the mine;
He will come along and ask you,
"Can you drill her off on time?"

4.
Drill your holes, boys; load them gently.
Light the first hole in the burn.
Light your cut holes and your kickers
And the knee holes in their turn.
Chorus

5.
Light your breast holes, light your side holes,
Light your lifters, center line.
Light your back holes—let's get going!
Make the corner, boys, on time.

Chorus

6.
There's your shots, boys; count them careful.
There's the loud report in the burn.
There's your cut holes and your kickers
And the knee holes in their turn.

7.
There's your breast holes, there's your side holes,
There's your back holes; we're in luck!
There's your lifters softly going,
Soft explosions under muck.

Author photo

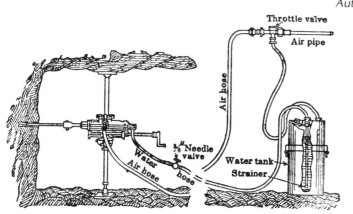

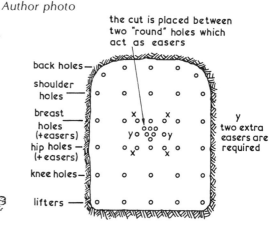

Left: Mounted drill with water tank
Right: A typical arrangement of holes in an 8 and 10 foot drift.

rock face where the miners are working is called a "stope." Since a vein of ore may run at an inclined angle to the drift or level, a drilling machine designed to operate primarily at angles above 30° is used; it is called a "stoper."

All three songs name jobs in the mine, listed here in their descending order of authority or prestige: mine captain, shifter or shift boss, "hard rock miner," chucker and mucker. The "mine captain" is the mine superintendent; the "shifter" is the shift boss or foreman; the "miner" drills and blasts the holes in the working face; the "chucker" is his assistant, handling the drills; and the lowly "mucker" has already been described. In the song "Hard Rock Miner," the miner take his identity in part from his status in the mine hierarchy. There is an added element of bigotry in this fragment from another verse of the same song:

"When I was a shifter,
The Bohunks called me mister..."

In "Taku Miner" another relationship among the occupations is indirectly stated. "Watch that light, boys," is a warning that the mine captain is approaching; he carries a lantern, unlike

Cont.

The song "Taku Miners" begins with two groups of miners changing shifts. Since they carry oil bottles, we know that they are going to the working faces in the mine, for the oil is to lubricate their compressed air percussion drills. Their job is not only the highly responsible one of drilling and blasting, but is the most hazardous of those underground. The group going to work descends the shaft by cage and awaits the foreman's instructions. His orders are simple—the job must be done by a specific time. Drilling and blasting are usually completed by the end of a shift. If the area of the blast is not well ventilated, some time may be needed for the noxious fumes to clear. Muckers can then go in to move the blasted rock.

These miners are under pressure. When one of them sees a low light, approaching, he gives the formula warning, "Watch that light, boys!" Everybody should then look as if they're highballing. The mine superintendent's query is heard as an oblique reminder to waste no time.

In the last line of the chorus when the miner exclaims, "Son-of-a-gun! This mining for gold!", he is reacting to a number of aspects of the work, not the least of which is the highballing pace with its multiplied dangers. This comment follows three lines, appropriately in jig time, in which the process of drilling a hole for explosives is depicted. We see the vertical bar and its horizontal arm on which the drilling machine is clamped. Below the arm is a nut called the dump which when loosened permits the drilling machine to be angled up or down. The bar is footed with a screw jack which enables the bar to be solidly held between the floor and roof of the stope. When the drilling machine is advanced as far as the dump, the hole is finished. The drilling process is deafening, repetitive, and fatiguing. Since, even today, about one-third of all underground accidents occur at the working face, the miner's general complaint is understandable.

To counter any speed-up, special care must be practised in all parts of the job. Danger from falling rock, the main cause of underground injury, can be minimized by scaling with a long steel rod the roof, the upper walls and the face of a stope, a process which shouldn't be hurried. After the holes are prepared, to load and prime them properly also needs care. Where fuses (instead of wire and electric current, which is common in large mines today) are used, as in "Taku Miners," they must be trimmed to the right lengths to ensure the proper order of firing. The drilling and firing pattern is chosen by the mine foreman to suit the size of the face and the hardness of the rock. As the shots fire in sequence, the miners count them carefully; any that fail may be delayed by a smouldering fuse. The miner in charge, a holder of a blaster's certificate, must see that no one goes near the face until conditions are safe. If there is any doubt whatsoever that all shots have fired, no one should return within thirty minutes of the time of lighting the fuse.

In the last stanza, the miner expresses pleasure that nothing has gone amiss. This may also mean the team are due a bonus in pay. Since these men are working for money, a bonus for rock broken beyond a specified amount or distance is another inducement to work quickly and efficiently. Such a prize, however, may tempt some to work in foolish haste. Safety must then depend on skilled and sensible workers and on rational safety regulations. Safety consciousness and good safety practice depend on a mature organized labor force, responsive government and its agencies, and progressive management.

For the Taku miners another aspect of life which would compel a reaction was the remoteness of the mine site. Access to the Polaris-Taku Mine was by plane from Juneau, Alaska, to the point where the Tulsequah River flows into the Taku River. From there a road led to the mine at Whitewater Creek, about six miles up the Tulsequah. The mining company provided a recreation hall, but those miners who wanted city attractions and could pay for them went to Juneau. "Taku Miners" is said to have been made up in the Juneau jail.

The opening of Polaris-Taku Mine in 1935 followed development which went back to the discovery in 1929 of mineralization along the canyon of Whitewater Creek. In 1937 a flotation mill was constructed to separate the gold from the ore. After being closed through wartime restrictions from 1942 to 1946, it re-opened and was in production until 1954. In this last period it was owned by Cominco Ltd.

"Loose the swing and jack the bar..." Drilling in stope at Rossland's Centre Star Mine, 1907.

Trimming a round before manually lighting the fuses.

41

B.C. Department of Mines

The lowly muckers.

I'm Only A Broken Down Mucker

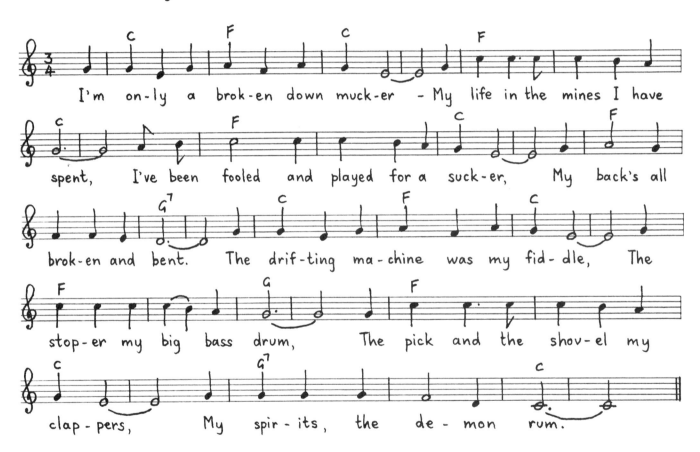

I'm on-ly a brok-en down muck-er - My life in the mines I have spent, I've been fooled and played for a suck-er, My back's all brok-en and bent. The drif-ting ma-chine was my fid-dle, The stop-er my big bass drum, The pick and the shov-el my clap-pers, My spir-its, the de-mon rum.

1.
I'm only a broken down mucker
My life in the mines I have spent.
I've been fooled and played for a sucker,
My back's all broken and bent.
The drifting machine was my fiddle,
The stoper my big bass drum,
The pick and the shovel my clappers,
My spirits, the demon rum.

2.
My youth was happy-go-lucky—
Scarlet women were my delight,
As soon as a wrong word was spoken
I'd put up my dukes and fight.
But pay-day was my hey-day—
On beer and rum I'd get drunk,
Then I'd wake up in the morning,
Broke and feeling so punk.

3.
I scoffed at the man in the office,
Called him belittlin' names.
But I realize now that I'm older
I used my back where he used his brains.
The drifting machine done for my hearing,
The mine gasses dimmed my sight.
I know my last days are nearing,
But I'll rally for one last fight.

4.
I'm only a broken down mucker—
My life in the mines I have spent,
I've been fooled and played for a sucker,
My back's all broken and bent.
I know my last days are nearing,
I know it only too well—
I'll be working and sweating and swearing
With a pick and shovel in Hell.

Fragments of the song "I'm Only a Broken-down Mucker" turned up in a number of widely separated places in British Columbia. What most informants remembered most readily were the first lines including,

"I've been fooled and played for a sucker."

The feeling of betrayal in this line makes the song much more than a complaint and presents a contradiction to the general tone of bravado. In the song, an all-but burnt-out laborer looks back on his life and concludes that he was duped, used, and somehow robbed of his human dignity. Who or what was responsible for this, he cannot say; but he hints at the existence of an unjust society.

It is well known that there is a strong tendency for children to find occupations in the same social class as their fathers. In the case of unskilled laborers, this pattern is most evident for they have benefited the least from the educational system, with its inherent service to middle-class notions of upward mobility and "free choice" in the selection of the occupation. The conflict between the values of their working class community and the school is often resolved by working-class children either by rejection of their language patterns together with the tastes and attitudes they share with their parents and neighbors, or by rejection of the school and all it stands for. To reject the school with its demeaning attitude towards him as a person (and as a member of his class), the working class child must build or affirm a set of values which saves his self-respect. For the male, often these values emphasize and exaggerate masculine stereotypes of independence and virility: the song, with its celebration of youth, its zest for physical labor, its whoring, fighting and drinking could well be a catalog of these traits. Crucial, too, in this list is the "belittlin'" of the office clerk—the man who chose the values of the school rather than those of his community.

The singer's portrayal of himself as a "broken-down mucker" with damage to his eyes, ears, and back conveys his realization that he can no longer fill the laborer's role. It seems to him now, as he reflects on his life, that he took the wrong path, that of "brawn" rather than "brain." But as we have seen, any other choice was, for all but a few, impossible. As is commonly the case, our mucker does not even ask how or why he ended up as he did. He has been so conditioned to individualistic and competitive views of the larger society that he accepts as his lot, however jocularly, an eternity in Hell with his pick and shovel—sweating, swearing and defying to the last a world that has so abused him. That he should consider this his reward after a lifetime of useful work is a sad reflection on a society which values people so little.

Cont. from P. 144

the workers whose lamps are attached to their head-gear.

Many dangers in the mine are quite easy to imagine. Rock falling from the roof or upper wall; accidents with explosives; problems when a charge fails to fire — redrilling near it could detonate it. What may not be so obvious is the danger done to a miner's lungs by rock dust, a siliceous material which the body tries to isolate with fibrous growths. The name of this disease, silicosis, first appears in a dictionary in 1890. The miners eventually called the early compressed-air hammer drills "widow-makers," for the machines had no device to control the dust they made. As little as two years of regular exposure to this dust could prove fatal.

Another danger found in the mine atmosphere is noxious gas produced by explosives. Ideally the chemical changes in the rapid oxidation of nitroglycerine (i.e. the explosion) leaves no poisonous gases. But explosions do not always follow theory. Early dynamites produced much unwanted carbon monoxide and nitrogen dioxide. A charge of dynamite which, owing to a failure of the detonator, burnt rather than exploded produced a cloud of nitrogen dioxide, known as "red fumes." Another explosive could release hydrogen sulphide. When either of these last gases comes into contact with the moisture in mucous membranes and lungs, it forms an acid destructive to human tissue. Contact with either may produce death; but, short of that, they may permanently damage eyes or lungs. In a lifetime in the mines some exposure is probably inevitable, but concentration and duration of contact are open to control. Since all explosives, even today, produce noxious gases, ventilation systems are of paramount importance.

*   *   *   *   *

147

Fishing For
Salmon & Halibut

Canada Dept. of Fisheries

History of the Pacific Halibut Fishery.

42

The Doryman

Oh, some can sit in their swiv-el chairs, 'Midst the cit-ies' rush and rum - our, And fret o'er the cares of the world af-fairs And the woes of the poor con-sum-er. But I don't en-vy such gild-ed ease; Just give me the salt -soaked o - cean breeze, The lift and surge of the white-capped seas, And the deck of a hal - i - but schoo - ner.

1.
Oh, some may sit in their swivel chairs,
'Midst the cities' rush and rumor,
And fret o'er the cares of the world affairs
And the woes of the poor customer
But I don't envy such gilded ease;
Just give me the salt-soaked ocean breeze,
The lift and surge of the white-capped seas,
And the deck of a halibut schooner.

2.
I want no fuss with the pale-faced cuss,
The clerk or piano tuner,
Who spend their lives in those stifling hives
In the struggle for more *mazuma*.   money
But give me the windswept ocean's space
Where the "flat ones" flop in the dory's waist
And the salt scud whips in your upturned face
As you pull for the side of the schooner.

3.
Yes, give me a packet that's sound and tight
And a skipper with guts to boom her,
Up under the heel of the Northern Lights
Where the grey seas strive to doom her.
Through the grinding ice, where the ground lines freeze,
Through the howling gales and the pounding seas—
For it's into such tranquil spots as these,
You must drive with a halibut schooner.
4.
We earn what we get, you may lay to that
Though we sometimes *"pull a boner"*;*
For the weather that's brewed of Yakutut,
It can change like a woman's humour.
When the *"queer thing"* flies to the schooner's truck.**
We slash our gear and damn our luck,
For we've time for naught but to cut and duck
For safety, aboard the schooner.
5.
And then, when our schooner is safe in port,
And we land in a boisterous humor,
We thank the gods that our stay is short
And wish we were leaving sooner.
We're rough and we're coarse and we're loud—what
 then?
We're the salt of the earth; we're dorymen
And tomorrow night we'll be off again
To the banks in a halibut schooner.

 * *make a mistake*
 ** *a warning signal, often a bucket*
   raised on the mast.

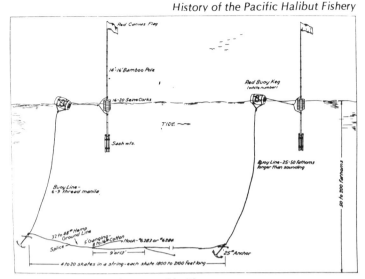

Diagram of halibut gear as set.

The song "The Doryman" in both its setting and its suggested characters typifies an important phase in the growth of the west coast halibut fishery. Although nothing is known directly of the origin of the song other than its accidental discovery on a halibut schooner in 1939, the scene it evokes can be given a general time and place, and the attitudes expressed by the singer belong to a doryman in that situation.

The song's recurring stanza-ending "halibut schooner" could apply to three different vessel designs. The first were the schooners brought round Cape Horn from Gloucester, Massachusetts, in the late 1880's to take part in the deep-sea sealing and also to try halibutting; they were quickly used to start the permanent commercial halibut industry. The other two vessel types evolved successively in the following twenty-five years. Though these, like the east coast schooners, carried dories, each had its distinctive features. Each vessel came about in response to particular demands of the fishery and incorporated the developing internal combustion engine.

To which vessel, then, does "The Doryman" refer? The information in the song that the fishing grounds are "off Yakutat" shows that the schooner was almost certainly of the third type, a large vessel first built about 1912, designed to face the open Pacific Ocean off the Alaskan coast and no longer primarily dependent on sail. In the move to more efficient and less hazardous ways of fishing, these schooners were further changed and the dories were obsolete by the mid-1930's. To see the song in its historical setting and to appreciate a doryman's life on this type of vessel, it will be helpful to view a sketch of the industry's early decades.

The Pacific halibut is a flatfish which lives and breeds on the continental shelf from northern California to the Bering Strait. Although a giant specimen could weigh 500 pounds and measure

Dorymen from the schooner Liberty in Burrard Inlet, North Vancouver in background. c. 1915.

The Fisherman.

seven feet in length, in the heyday of the west coast halibut fishery a 300 pounder was thought of as very large and the average was about 60 pounds. The halibut became the base of a thriving fishery only after the transcontinental railroads reached the northwest coast—the C.P.R. at Vancouver and the Northern Pacific at Tacoma in 1887; the Great Northern at Seattle in 1893; and, much later but of great importance, the Grand Trunk Pacific at Prince Rupert in 1914. Halibut makes a tasty table dish providing it is fresh or, at second best, fresh-frozen. With the rail connection it could be carried in refrigerated cars to Boston and New York where the main American fish distributors were located. The challenge of catching enough fish and keeping them fresh has, over the years, determined the fishing grounds, the overall fishing methods, and the supporting shore facilities, such as ice manufacturing and cold storage plants.

Although halibut may be caught on a simple handline with baited hook, the permanent commercial fishery depended at its start and for several decades on a technique using dories and ground lines, a practice brought from New England. Dorymen paid out and hauled in gear made up of lines each about 2000 feet long with baited hooks spaced 9 feet apart. The number of these lengths of line, or "skates," that dorymen handled in a day was limited by the hours of daylight, the weather, and the size of the catch. Each day the fish was dressed and stored in chipped ice (one pound of ice for each pound of fish) in the hold of the parent vessel. When desired the dories could be nested one within another on the ship's deck. This method of fishing was discarded as vessels became more and more mechanized. With the controlling power of diesel engines replacing the oars of the dorymen, long lines of skates attached end to end (as many as twenty at a time) were paid out and mechanically picked up. By 1930 the ground line and dory had all but been replaced by the long line. This shift had been part of the larger change from sailing schooners to self-contained diesel-run vessels needed for economical exploitation of the truly deep-sea grounds on the continental shelf.

The beginning of the west-coast halibut fishery was marked in 1889 by

The Jennie F. Decker, a Gloucester schooner of the type used at the beginning of the commercial halibut industry.

Small northwest coast halibut schooner, rigged for sails but with an auxiliary engine.

The halibut schooner Liberty in Burrard Inlet with a dory swinging from the boom. Prospect Point and First Narrows in background. c. 1915. These vessels, known as "smokeboats," used their sails primarily as stabilizers.

a rail shipment through Tacoma to the eastern market. That this first carload was rotting on arrival pointed out sharply the need for plenty of ice and the least delay possible in delivery. After solving these problems, numbers of New England schooners and sloops based in Seattle and Tacoma fished Puget Sound, the Georgia Strait, and the Strait of Juan de Fuca. In favorable weather some schooners ventured to fish the banks in the open water outside the Strait of Juan de Fuca. Fishing beyond Cape Flattery was not only hazardous, but, when the winds were weak or contrary, the trip to port took too long. To answer the need for a vessel which was more maneuverable than the large Gloucester schooners in the narrow channels and inlets, smaller schooners, similar in design to the east coast craft, were soon built, and, as early as 1894, were fitted with internal combustion engines. These fished out of the Puget Sound ports from spring to fall and moved north to the inside waters of southern Alaska in the winter, sending the fish south by steamer. In 1901 there were some twenty small schooners and sloops remaining year-round in Alaskan waters. By 1903 nearly all these small two-dory schooners in the fishery had auxiliary engines.

As Puget Sound's schooner-based industry grew and reached into southern Alaskan waters, a fishery of a different character developed out of Vancouver. Although Vancouver's fishery was early served by a few sloops, from its beginning in 1892 it used steamers as parent ships. They could carry a large catch and navigate readily through the narrow coastal channels. Thus, the steamers, despite wind and weather, plied regularly back and forth through the long, narrow passages between Vancouver Island and the mainland from halibut grounds in Queen Charlotte Sound, Hecate Strait, and Dixon Entrance. For flexibility, in 1895 the steamer operators adopted dories as their collecting boats. The impact of steamer fishing was early grasped by a group of Boston fish wholesalers, owners of the New England Fish Company. With finance capital and market control, the Company operated out of Vancouver in 1893, and in a few years it and its subsidiaries had monopolized all steamer operations in Vancouver, New Westminster and, later, in Prince Rupert.

Steamers, or "company boats," as they came to be called, together with the auxiliary-powered schooners, took as much halibut as the increasing eastern market could handle. At first the steamers operated only during the winter months, making up the seasonal decline of the Atlantic fishery. But as overfishing reduced the overall output of the Atlantic fishery and as cold storage facilities were built on the west coast, more and more vessels worked the west coast fishery year-round. With such intense fishing, it is not surprising that by 1910 the grounds began to be depleted. For two decades vessels and methods had been adapted to fish new grounds as they were discovered; now the limits of the more or less protected waters had been reached. In some places such as Puget Sound the halibut had largely disappeared. In 1910 while the small schooners continued fishing on grounds still profitable to them, the steamers began to operate in the waters exposed to the Pacific from Oregon to southern Alaska.

The fishery would soon have declined drastically had not two events then taken place. First, new halibut banks were discovered further up the coast; of special note in 1912 was the finding of Yakutat Spit. Since the new grounds were accessible only to the steamers, the second event followed: the designing of a new type of schooner, a large vessel fitted with a gas engine using sail only as auxiliary power and as a stabilizer. This was the third type of halibut schooner, the only one capable of working steadily on the new deep-sea banks. Its lines were more those of an engine-powered vessel, yet, like its predecessors, it had two masts: the foremast rigged for sail, but the mainmast rigged as a derrick. At the stern aft of the pilot house were nested six or seven dories.

A boom in the construction of these new vessels peaked in 1913-14. They were owned primarily by fishermen and were often financed by supply companies or small investors in search of high profits; a few were owned by the fish companies.

Although the company-owned steamer fleet of eighteen vessels in 1913 dwindled to four by 1921, the number of company schooners remained small—independent owners came to dominate the fishery. High among the reasons for this success was that a captain-owner enjoyed dual motivation; as skilled seaman and fisherman he received both the owner's and the skipper's shares. A further motivation lay in the fact that the more a captain and crew, including the dorymen, worked as a team, the better off they all were. Their common interest was maintained right through to the sale of the catch to a fish company. The fish auction could present rough weather too; for fish companies, when dealing with independent vessels, used all their resources to buy as cheaply as possible. Since fish for freezing sold for less than that for the fresh market, when good fish arrived at port in abundance the fishermen's price was open to manipulation or collusion in bidding. It was thus to the companies' advantage to deal with fishermen not in their employ. As a result of shared fortunes and misfortunes, the bond between the captain and the crew became an important factor in determining the success of these deep-sea fishermen-owned schooners. It is the spirit and attitude of these men which is expressed in "The Doryman."

In the dozen years following 1912, many changes—in addition to the rise of these new halibut schooners—took place in the industry, changes affecting fishermen, vessels, owners, companies, governments and, first and last in importance, the halibut.

In 1912 halibut fishermen reorganized their union, renamed the Deep Sea Fishermen's Union, and were able to bargain successfully for a greater share of the catch—four-fifths instead of three-quarters. To do this they shut down steamer operation in Vancouver and New Westminster for five months in the winter of 1913-14. They later negotiated an agreement in which the vessel owners shared the cost of the gear (lines, hooks, etc.). Until then the dorymen bore the whole loss in situations such as that in the song, when a sudden storm forced them to "slash [their] gear" and "cut and duck for safety..." In 1913 the schooner owners formed an organization to meet with fish dealers, on the one hand, and with fishermen on the other.

In the fall of 1914 the Grand Trunk Pacific Railway carred its first halibut east from Prince Rupert. The new terminus had been preparing for this task since the founding of the city in 1909 and had ready the largest fish freezing plant in the world. Until the completion of the railway, all fish went south by steamer to Vancouver and Seattle.

Pacific halibut
hippglottis stenolepis

Three commercial sizes:
chicken (up to 10 lbs.)
medium (10 to 60 lbs.)
large   (over 60 lbs.)

A stimulus to the build-up of the Canadian fleet at Prince Rupert came in 1913, when the American customs dropped the duty on Canadian halibut. In December, 1914, the Canadian government granted U.S. vessels permission to freight their catch by rail from Prince Rupert in bond, a privilege Americans had been accorded in Vancouver since 1897. The fishery was so active in 1914 and 1915 that it suffered from overproduction and prices dropped..

The need for regulation of the fishery was becoming obvious. Not only did winter fishing on the new grounds off Yakutat interfere with the halibut spawning, but the spawning halibut were not of top quality. Three studies of the Pacific halibut fishery, published by the British Columbia government (1916-1917), showed graphically how uncontrolled exploitation depleted the resource. A closed winter season was suggested, but, although some vessel owners undertook voluntary restrictions, an effective policy was not forthcoming until representatives of the Canadian and American governments came up with an agreement in 1922 on a closed season. This agreement was the only firm commitment to action in "the Treaty between the United States and Great Britain for the Preservation of the Northern Pacific Halibut Fishery." The treaty, signed in 1923, also set up the International Fisheries Commission, which later became the International Pacific Halibut Commission, a parallel body to that which manages salmon. This treaty, incidentally, is claimed to be the "first international treaty signed by Canada on its own as an independent nation of the British Commonwealth" (see *Canada Year Book 1972*, p. 687).

Perhaps owing to the fact that American fishermen accounted for some four-fifths of the halibutting and that the big halibut dealers were American owned, Canadians held a weak position in negotiating reciprocal rights in such matters as port privileges, including the purchase of bait and ice, and the hiring of crews. The tenuous reciprocity of the war years had completely evaporated by 1922, when the U.S. Customs reimposed a two cent per pound duty on Canadian halibut. The result of the discrimination was that the fleets of the two countries fished for their own markets.

The halibut schooner soon adopted more powerful diesel-fueled engines. Their dories disappeared, their generators enabled the fishermen to work at night, and in the early 1930's some were modified to work as seiners. Although by the early 1940's the halibut dorymen belonged to the past, men today are still drawn by the challenge of halibutting in the northeast Pacific.

B.C. Provincial Archives

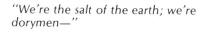

"We're the salt of the earth; we're dorymen—"

154

Rivers Inlet, c. 1930.

43

The Song Of The Sockeye

Oh, hark to the song of the sock-eye Like a sir-en's call of old; When it gets in your blood you can't shake it: It's the same as the fev-er for gold.

1.
Oh, hark to the song of the sockeye
Like a siren's call of old;
When it gets in your blood you can't shake it:
It's the same as the fever for gold.

2.
There's a hole in the B.C. coastline,
Rivers Inlet's the place I mean;
And it's there you will find the old timer
And also the fellow who's green.

3.
Oh, the boats head for there like the sockeye
And some are a joy to the eye,
While others are simply abortions,
And ought to be left high and dry.

4.
Now they go to the different canneries
And before they can make one haul
It's three hundred bucks for net, grub and gas
Which they hope to pay off before fall.

5.
Then it's off to the head of the inlet
At six o'clock, Sunday night,
But when morning comes and you've got about three,
The prospects don't look very bright.

6.
Of course, there is always an alibi
To account for a very poor run—
The weather is wrong, the moon's not full,
Or the big tides will help the fish come.

7.
Now, along about dusk when you're starting to doze
And you think you've got a good night's set,
An engine will roar, and you look out the door
As some *"farmer"* tows into your net.   *"tug boat"*

8.
Now some of us think of the future,
While others have things to forget,
But most of us sit here and think of a school
Of sockeye hitting the net.

9.
And when the season is over
And you figure out what you have made,
You were better off working for wages,
No matter how low you were paid.

10.
For the comforts of home are worth something,
So take it from me, my friend,
Frying-pan grub and no head room
Will ruin your health in the end.

11.
So hark to the song of the sockeye
Like a siren's call of old;
When it gets in your blood you can't shake it:
It's the same as the fever for gold.

Mr. Ross Cumbers at Coal Harbour, Vancouver, in 1941, two years after he wrote "The Song of the Sockeye."

"Then it's off to the head of the inlet At six o'clock, Sunday night..."—a Fishery officer firing a bomb, Skeena River, B.C., c. 1930, a procedure used both to open the week's fishing at 6 p.m. Sunday and to close it at 6 p.m. Friday. Bluestone (copper sulphate) tanks in photo are for soaking linen nets.

The sockeye salmon with its red color, its firm flesh and its choice flavor is a highly prized commercial fish on the northwest coast. Canning began in British Columbia in the 1870's and by 1900 the fishing industry was packing annually millions of cases of salmon; by then the industry was dominated by consolidated packing companies employing seasonal workers. The main change in this pattern today is that while the packing business is even more concentrated the fishermen are well integrated for bargaining through their union, the U.F.A.W.U.—The United Fishermen and Allied Workers' Union.

All five species of salmon of the northwest coast have a common destiny in that they hatch in fresh water, proceed to the Pacific Ocean and at maturity return to spawn in the waters where they hatched; fish of all but one of the species then die. The sockeye, a fish which does not readily take bait, is caught at maturity at the mouths of rivers as it proceeds on its spawning migration. So strong is the fish's urge to go forward that when a broad-meshed net is placed in front of it, a migrating sockeye will force its head into the net opening, ensnaring itself by the gills.

The gill-net, made of linen or nylon thread, is set out behind the boat, supported by a line of floats or corks at the top and held down by a line of lead sinkers at the bottom. It is about six hundred feet long and twenty to thirty feet deep. The nets were hauled in by hand until large wooden drums on which they could be wound were fitted to engine-powered boats. As the net was brought aboard, the enmeshed fish were removed, to be transferred later to a cannery packing boat.

The economic position of the gill-net fisherman is parallel to that of a farmer. The farmer depends on a return from his labor and his investment in land and equipment; the fisherman hopes for a return from his labour with his boat and net. For the short Rivers Inlet season in 1939, a fishermen required about three hundred dollars to invest in his net, food and fuel. Today it costs over a thousand dollars for the six-week season.

The prototype of the west coast gill-net fishing boat was the Columbia River skiff, the first of which was built about a hundred years ago by an unknown craftsman. The early boats were some twenty feet long, heavily built, with broad beam and a slightly raised bow. Before engines were common, the cannery-owned skiffs were towed to the fishing grounds by a packing boat. The fishermen would stay on the grounds for the regulated fishing week which was from 6 p.m. Sunday until Friday, when they would be towed back to the cannery. Shelter on these boats was under a piece of canvas stretched over an oar fastened to the mast, and the cooking was done on a primus stove. When engines and cabins were added to the skiffs, although there was greater mobility and independence for the fisherman, living conditions on board were cramped and unhealthy. Now boats are often over thirty feet long and are much more satisfactory to live on.

44

The Pender Harbour Fisherman

Come all ye jol-ly listen-ers and hear me while I hum; A stor-y I will tell you of the sal-ty fish-er-man. From all the lit-tle riv-ers and in-lets of the coast He seems to like Pen-der Har-bour to bum a-round the most.

1.
Come all ye jolly listeners and hear me while I hum;
A story I will tell you of the salty fisherman.
From all the little rivers and inlets of the coast
He seems to like Pender Harbour to bum around the
     most.

2.
Oh, early on a summer's morn when the breakers
     pound,
He eases from his greasy bunk and gazes all around.
The sky's a little cloudy and breezes fan the sea;
He crawls again into his cave, a breakfast for the flea.

3.
Or he may crank his lemon and through the waters
     plough
To swing bull some and gossip over at the scow.
They never wash their carcasses; that's why they always
     drown;
The bilge, the grease, the weight of fleas always drag
     them down.

4.
They wear their shirts until they rot and fall into the
     chuck;
Their feet stick out of rubber boots, their pants them-
     selves could walk.
Most of them are lazy born; others say they're tired.
They walk a slow and shuffling gait as if their feet were
     mired.

5.
Siwash bums, quarterbreeds, big Swedes, Scots and
     Poles,
The scum of many different blends that should be on
     the coals.
One always smells a fisherman before he's seen or
     heard.
He leads a free and careless life; Oh, what a funny bird!

6.
They tell you stories by the mile of fish that they have
     nailed;
They tell you of creatures of the deep and of the seas
     they've sailed.
Now, all you jolly listeners, believe me if you can—
It's all the truth I'm telling you, 'cause I'm a fisherman.

N.F.B. photo

Pender Harbour with its sheltered moorage and strategic location was a natural settlement for fishermen and loggers in the early part of the century. A tightly-knit community developed around its many bays and little inlets. Since it was brought together by water transportation, some called it the "Venice of the North." For decades the twin resources of forests and fish maintained a resilient economy. The loggers and fishermen enjoyed a friendly rivalry, making jokes at each other's expense and, on community picnics, even pulling a tug-o'-war, loggers vs. fishermen.

"The Pender Harbour Fisherman" is an example of this good-natured rivalry for, although the words of the song say it was made up by a fisherman, it was in fact the work of members of a logging family. The song, in spite of its exaggeration, does however reflect the conditions as they commonly existed on small gillnetters and trollers in the 1930's. Instead of looking at the history, function and design of these fishboats to explain the cramped living conditions, the song scurrilously puts the blame on the character of the fishermen themselves.

The song takes the tune and the form of the first verse from Harry "Mac" McClintock's "The Bum Song," recorded on a 78 r.p.m. disc about 1930.

"They tell you stories by the mile of fish that they have nailed." A cannery worker holding a 73 pound spring salmon at Steveston, B.C., 1963.

Author photo

*"From all the little rivers and inlets of the coast
He seems to like Pender Harbour to bum around the most..."*

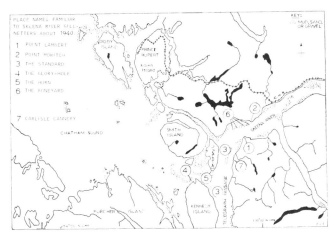

Bring Back That Gill Net To Me

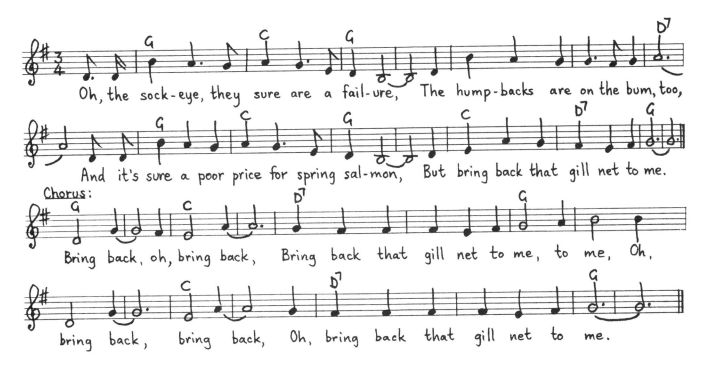

Oh, the sock-eye, they sure are a fail-ure, The hump-backs are on the bum, too, And it's sure a poor price for spring sal-mon, But bring back that gill net to me.

Chorus: Bring back, oh, bring back, Bring back that gill net to me, to me, Oh, bring back, bring back, Oh, bring back that gill net to me.

1.
Oh, the sockeye they sure are a failure,
The humpbacks are on the bum, too,
And it's sure a poor price for spring salmon,
But bring back that gill net to me.

Chorus
Bring back, oh, bring back,
Oh, bring back that gill net to me, to me.
Bring back, oh, bring back,
Oh, bring back that gill net to me.

2.
I think we'll make a drift at Port Lambert,
Or else take a rap at the Rip,
And then take a shot at Point Mowitch,
So bring back that gill net to me.

3.
The Standard's the drift on the river,
For the Glory-hole the boys make a rush,
But going round the Horn's got them all beat
So bring back that gill net to me.

4.
There's a place on the river called the Boneyard,
Keep away from the old snaggy bar,
Make sure, boys, you've thrown in the right place,
So bring back that gill net to me.

5.
Of the canneries there's one I favor,
And that is old Carlisle, you see,
For the workers, they sure know their onions
And the whole gang goes out on a spree.

Linen nets were mended on Saturday mornings for about four or five hours. They would be soaked for an hour in a bluestone solution before being returned to the gillnetters.

Leo Harris made up this song in the summer of 1939 while fishing for the Canadian Fishing Co.'s Carlisle cannery, which was near the mouth of the Skeena River. He sang it at Saturday night dances and parties at the cannery; and the gathering of fishermen, many accompanied by their wives, joined him in the chorus with its affirmation that, despite the ups-and-downs of a fisherman's lot, he will keep on fishing.

Throughout his working life, Leo Harris did just that. He began fishing on the Skeena at the Carlisle cannery in 1926. In 1928 he operated his first gas boat, a Vancouver-based, company-owned 28-footer with a 5 h.p. Easthope engine. He took it up the coast to the Skeena in the late spring and returned to Vancouver with it in the fall. That pattern he followed until he retired in 1964 at the age of 62.

He recalled that for seven of those early years he used a 26-footer with a 4 h.p. Vivian engine, a contrast to the larger and speedier vessel he operated in the 1960's. The same changes in technology eventually made the Carlisle cannery obsolete, and since Leo's retirement, it has been torn down. With the cannery went the small cabins allotted to the fishermen by the cannery, one of which had been Leo's for so many years.

The song begins with a list of typical complaints over poor runs and low prices; the former could only be solved by conservation methods, the latter by union negotiations with the companies. Three of the salmon species which are caught on the coast are mentioned: the sockeye (or red), the humpback (humpies or pink), and the spring (chinook, king or tyee) salmon. The other two are the chum (dog or keta) and the coho (silver, or blueback for the immature) salmon. The names vary in time and place and among persons on the coast from Alaska to Oregon.

The local place names are those used by the salmon fishermen. On the map today, Point Lambert is 4 km. to the south of Veitch Point and near the former site of the Carlisle cannery. In the song and on the map printed here, Point Lambert is another name for Veitch Point. The alternate name occurred in pilot guides early in the century, but Point Lambert persisted among some fishermen.

"Of the canneries there's one that I favor, and that is old Carlisle..." One of the twenty-three canneries from Alaska to Oregon operated by the U.S.-owned New England Fishery Co. and its Canadian subsidiary, the Canadian Fishing Co. in 1947.

Ranching: Dairy & Cattle

Dairy herd, near Duncan, Vancouver Island, c. 1900.

The Young British Rancher

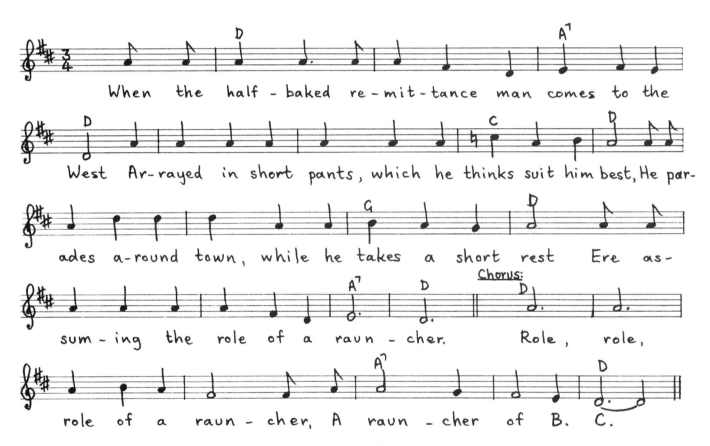

When the half-baked re-mit-tance man comes to the West Ar-rayed in short pants, which he thinks suit him best, He par-ades a-round town, while he takes a short rest Ere as-sum-ing the role of a raun-cher. Role, role, role of a raun-cher, A raun-cher of B. C.

1.
When the half-baked remittance man comes to the West
Arrayed in short pants, which he thinks suit him best,
He parades around town, while he takes a short rest
Ere assuming the role of a rancher.

Chorus
Role, role, role of a rancher,
A rancher of B.C.

2.
Now all you remittance men listen to me
And I'll give you some pointers as far as I may
Which might make you a rancher if you will obey,
A rancher that's fit for a rancher.

Fit, fit, fit for a rancher, etc.

3.
First, mind you don't stay in Victoria long;
The water is bad and the liquor is strong,
And as you must drink something, you're sure to go
    wrong,
And spoil your success as a rancher.

'Cess, 'cess, 'cess as a rancher, etc.

4.
Take advice if you buy a fine ranch by a stream,
Don't leave for trout fishing your cows and your cream,
But make butter and wealth beyond your greediest
    dream,
Which is far the best plan for a rancher.

Plan, plan, plan for a rancher, etc.

5.
If when riding your bronco he starts in to buck,
And you fear if you fall by his hoofs you'll be struck,
Throw your arms round his neck, man, and trust to
    your luck,
If you can't keep your seat like a rancher.
Seat, seat, seat like a rancher, etc.

6.
If in hunting for deer on some lone mountain top
Across a big bear you should happen to drop,
Just climb the first tree and be sure there to stop
Till assistance arrives for the rancher.
'Rives, 'rives, 'rives for the rancher, etc.

7.
If in clearing the stumps of your ranch there's a hitch
Don't call your stump-puller a contrary bitch,
She's human as you are, you treat her as sich,
And she'll work for the young British rancher.
Young, young, young British rancher, etc.

8.
If after long striving on Vancouver's plains
You find that your debts are the whole of your gains
Go up to the Klondike with the cash that remains,
And get better off than a rancher.
Off, off, off than a rancher, etc.

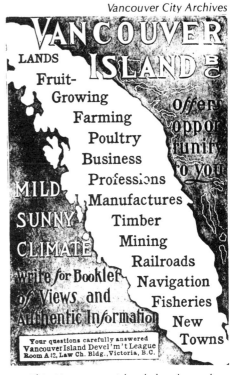

This Vancouver Island developers' ad appeared in Westward Ho (Oct. 1909), a dozen years after the verse was written.

In 1897 about 80% of B.C.'s people were of English, Scots, and Irish origin, and of these more than half were English. Although many of them had come by way of eastern Canada and the U.S.A., a good number of the recent arrivals came directly from "The Old Country." About the year 1900, according to Major J.S. Matthews, late Vancouver city archivist, some employers, when advertising jobs, stipulated that "No Englishman Need Apply." Recognition of two notable types of British immigrants of that time should help to explain this phenomenon.

According to historian Margaret Ormsby, one was the workingman: the printer, the railwayman and the miner who came to ply his trade "to swell the ranks of trade unions and provide leadership for a political labor movement." The other was a product of families far enough up England's class ladder to support their youngest sons, who were sent out to the "colonies" to build a life for themselves or, if they were ne'er-do-wells, to avoid disgracing the family further at home. The title "rancher" carried with it a proprietary air attractive to the "upper classes," and although many of these men had no practical background, they were destined by their parents to become "young British ranchers." Thus with a regular cheque or remittance from home these Englishmen had a specially subsidized opportunity to go into dairy, small fruit, tree fruit and cattle ranching. Living on unequal terms financially, projecting a class image as they formed "rancher's clubs" for themselves and private schools for their children, and maintaining superior attitudes in a country that generally rejected pretensions of birth, the remittance men were resented by much of the populace.

The dislike for the British workingmen in some quarters arose from fear of militant unionism and Socialism. On the matter of attitudes towards English immigrants, historian Margaret Ormsby writes, quoting from a 1905 periodical:

> Almost more disliked than union organizers or socialists were remittance men—those "unfortunates" who were to be found in every portion of the Empire, but whose "real home is in British Columbia, which seems to afford them their natural resting place."

(Ormsby, B.C.: A History, p. 329)

Victorians saw many of the upper class English pass through their city on the way to settle in Duncan, the Cowichan Valley, Parksville, Comox or Courtenay. They were often retired officers from the Imperial Army or Royal Navy; others were remittance men.

47

Branding calves, Okanagan, c. 1910.

Sunset

Come shades of dead cow-boys, once care-free young cow-boys,
Dead ghosts of old com-rades I rode with so long. When
life was be-fore us, we rode oft in chor-us — Old
ghosts do you hear now the lone wolf's last song?

1.
Come, shades of dead cowboys, once carefree young
    cowboys,
Dead ghosts of old comrades I rode with so long,
When life was before us, we rode oft in chorus—
Old ghosts, do you hear now the lone wolf's last song?
2.
I'm an old high-heeled cowboy, an old has-been cowboy,
For long o'er the prairies I've roamed far and wide.
But my last campfire's blazing, my old eyes fast glazing—
I rode my last bronco and rode my last ride.

3.
My campfire is crowded with faces smoke-shrouded,
But all are ghost faces of comrades I knew.
My turn's come to die, ghosts, with no human by,
    ghosts—
The gate is before me and soon I'll pass through.
4.
I'm a fast sinking cowboy, a poor lonesome cowboy,
Who'll soon pass to judgement his sins to atone.
When the gate swings behind me, may Christ's mercy
    find me—
He knows it's blame lonely to die slow alone.

Although "Sunset" has not turned up in any collection of cowboy songs, it sounds like an old song. Its image of passing through a ranch gate like herded cattle as a metaphor for dying, together with its simply-stated belief in an afterlife, the Judgment, and the atonement of sins through Christ's mercy, is reminiscent of the concept found in "The Grand Roundup." "Sunset" was one of the many old songs known by Mrs. Kate Lacey, who lived in Osoyoos, B.C.

The song begins with an exhortation, but the image of the prairie campfire in the second stanza marks the change of mood to that of a reverie. In the first stanza the old cowboy asks the ghosts of his comrades if they hear him singing. He, like an old wolf separated from his pack, is giving his last howl. The wolf, like the blazing campfire, belongs to the open prairies. Both will die. The title "Sunset" serves as a further symbol of the naturalness of death.

The double rhymes in the verse pattern introduce to each stanza parallel phrasing which effectively contrasts and emphasizes certain notions: "dead cowboys...young cowboys," "high-heeled cowboy." By these and other devices the ideas of youth and age, of separation and loneliness, are introduced and sustained to the last line of the song.

Another song might limit its theme to the feelings of being alone and suffering loneliness, the state which causes some old people who have outlived their friends to utter the plaint, "I have lived too long." The Christian framework brought into the song in the second-to-last line introduces a popular way of confronting death. But the old cowboy, bereft of his comrades and no longer able to ride, implies that his sins, which perhaps include an impatience for death, will be forgiven through Christ's sympathy. Christ will have mercy on him, for His death on the cross was also slow and alone.

Alta S. Fife, the noted specialist on cowboy songs, on seeing this text wondered if the original ending had been either the grammatically correct "slowly alone" or the similar sounding "so alone." After reading the note on "slow(ly)" in H.W. Fowler's *Modern English Usage*, and rereading the text, I accept "slow alone" as appropriate, but acknowledge singers may want to use one of the other suggested endings.

B.C. Provincial Archives

48

Larry Massy, butt of this humorous song, is a sober rancher, and today fights to protect the Deadman against the incursions of loggers.

Tying A Knot In The Devil's Tail

Oh, high up on the Dead-man, Where the jack pine trees grow tall, Bruce Webb and Lar-ry Mas-sy Had a round-up way last fall.

1.
Oh, high up on the Deadman,
Where the jack pine trees grow tall,
Bruce Webb and Larry Massy
Had a round-up way last fall.

2.
Now every little doggie with the big long ears
That chanced to come their way,
Oh, his little ears wriggled and his little hide sizzled
In a most artistic way.

3.
Said Bruce Webb to Larry,
"I think I'll take a ride."
For it was in the days, boys,
A man could sure oil his insides.

4.
They headed for the Savona bar
Way down on Whisky Row—
Ended up way late that night
Some fifty drinks below.

5.
The house it ordered up a round
And headed them down the road;
And who should they meet but the Devil himself
Come a-joggin' down the road.

6.
"Come all you ornery cowboys,
You better hunt your holes;
For I am the old Devil himself,
And I've come to collect your souls."

7.
Said Bruce Webb to the Devil,
"I know us boys are tight,
But before you collect our souls,
You'll have one heck of a fight!"

8.
So he took down his rope and he built him a loop,
And he cast it straight and true;
And he caught the Devil by his two horns,
And he pulled his dallies through.

9.
Now Larry Massy was a lariat man
With a hemp rope coiled so neat;
Took down his rope and he cast his loop,
Caught the Devil by his two hind legs.

10.
They stretched him out right there on the road
While the running irons grew hot;
With a whoop and a holler and a half silver dollar,
They branded him on the spot.

11.
They tied nine knots in the old Devil's tail,
And for a joke they turned him loose;
And he got up and he loped to the shade,
To the shade of a mountain spruce.

12.
Now if you ever ride up on the Deadman,
And you hear one hell of a wail,
You'll know it's the Devil howling from the pain
Of the knots tied in his tail.

Author photo

Ronnie Craig, rancher, made this song fit "The Deadman."

On the map, Deadman River (the locals call it Deadman Creek) runs some forty miles south to join the Thompson River a few miles west of Savona, which is situated at the west end of Kamloops Lake. To the east of Deadman River are Criss Creek and Tranquille River, both of which flow south into Kamloops Lake. The region that these three streams drain has a varying surface, rolling, hilly and hummocky in some parts and a plateau in another. The maximum annual rainfall of fifteen to twenty inches produces sufficient vegetation for grazing livestock. Where grass yields to open forest, the trees are mainly jack pine, with some poplar, willow, spruce and alder. Deadman River in its upper-middle reaches flows along a narrow, densely-wooded depression with several delightful lakes, a contrast with the general landscape. Below the lakes are a number of ranches which produce hay for their beef cattle which spend most of the year on licenced rangeland in the region.

A start in farming and ranching in the Deadman River and Criss Creek valleys was made between 1910 and 1920. Some of the land was homesteaded under the British Columbia Land Act and other pieces were purchased. Two generations later, much improvement has been made to the haying land by drainage and irrigation. The population is still small. The nearest store and post office for Deadman ranches are at Savona.

The ranchers get together for a party about once a year, probably occasioned by some shared event such as somebody leaving. Ronnie Craig has sung his reworking of "Tying a Knot in the Devil's Tail" at these gatherings. The names that appear in the song are ranchers or one-time ranchers of "the Deadman."

49

Hangin' In The Barn

Chorus
Oh, it's hangin' in the barn, and a-hangin' on the horn—
There's a split-eared bridle that's not new.
There's a long-shanked pair of spurs that we riders used to
    use
With that old saddle hangin' in the barn.

1.
But the days have come and gone, and the jeep has took
    our place,
And Turner Valley gasoline is stinkin' up the range.
But it makes you kind of lonesome when you walk
    around some place
And see an old bronc saddle just a-hangin' in the barn.

2.
And when my days on earth have ended, and I reach the
    great divide,
And when I see old Saint Peter by the gate,
I will ask him if he'll have the angels sing this song
Of the saddle that's just hangin' in the barn.

The chorus of "Hangin' in the Barn" presents the kind of picture that might be reconstructed in a good museum display. It evokes a sense of the time before the jeep displaced the horse on most ranches, a time when horse-power was warm, sweaty, and vibrant with life. Then the skilled hands of the craftsmen—the saddle and harness makers, and the blacksmiths—shaped the gear, which was in turn known through the hands of the cowboys. The makers, the riders and their mounts all knew the weight, shape and texture of the gear. It became a symbol for the traditional methods of handling cattle. The song does not mention the rough life of the cowboy, but through the chorus it strongly stirs nostalgia for this simpler and more cohesive life.

A double irony in the song lies in the fact that the fuel which made possible the mechanization of the cattle range, also spewed its odor over the grassy foot-hill country where gas and oil were discovered. such as in the Turner Valley southwest of Calgary. Gas was found there in 1914, but the Turner Valley field was not greatly developed until after oil was discovered in 1936. The gas that rushed out of the many new oil wells, which were soon drilled, was wastefully burned off. Its heavy sulphurous smell reached as far as Calgary on a bad day, but the air of Turner Valley ranchland was affected most of the time.

Jeeps were designed and produced by Willys-Overland for the U.S. military in 1942. These four-wheel-drive vehicles, 11 ft. long and 4 ft. high, proved their adaptability, and at the war's end appeared as a flexible work-horse in many places, among which were the cattle ranches. Following the introduction of these vehicles would come many other changes in the handling and raising of beef cattle, changes which would rationalize production for efficiency and profit but which, at the same time, would further depersonalize, and complicate the cattle handlers' lives.

The most far-reaching of the changes was in the method of feeding the animals. It was now possible to ready steers for market in about twenty-one months, instead of the three years required for grass-fed cattle. Calves were either killed, sold off, or wintered, to be removed to feedlots during the following year for "finishing" in one hundred days. The ranch routine was thus brought nearer to the impersonal efficiency of the slaughterhouse; the old rhythms and relationships in a cowboy's life were gone. In "Hangin' in the Barn" the only word the cowboy finds for his reaction to all these changes is the nostalgic "lonesome."

The song was brought into the southern interior of British Columbia from Alberta where it had been composed by a one-time Turner Valley cowboy.

Author photo

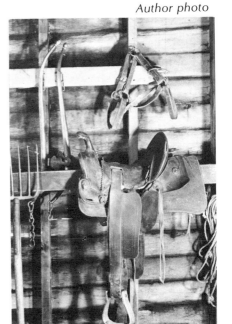

Hangin' in the barn—a well-worn western or stock saddle stamped: "W.C. Reeder—maker—Ritzville, Wash."

Sources of Text, Tunes and Emendations

Abbreviations used in this Appendix

BCHQ — British Columbia Historical Quarterly

LAWLESS — Ray M. Lawless, *Folksingers and Folksongs In America*, New York: Duell, Sloan and Pearce, 1960.

LAWS — Malcolm G. Laws, Jr., *Native American Balladry*, Revised edition (for Song-types A-I), Philadelphia: American Folklore Society, 1964 and *American Balladry from British Broadsides*, (for Song-types J-Q) Philadelphia: American Folklore Society.

LINGENFELTER — Richard E. Lingenfelter and Richard A. Dwyer, eds., *Songs of the American West*, Berkeley: Univeristy of California Press, 1968.

PABC — Public Archives of British Columbia

PJT — Philip J. Thomas

PJT Coll. — The Philip J. Thomas Tape Collection, Aural History Archives, PABC.

SAWNEY — James Anderson (sic), *Sawney's Letters and Cariboo Rhymes*, repr. Victoria, 1962.

1.

The Bold Northwestman. W. from broadside "Bold Northwestman and Wandering Boys of Switzerland" at Harvard University (Widener Library). M. from George Herzog's notation of "The Northwesterman" as he collected it from the singing of Fred Nesbitt, St. Stephen, New Brunswick in 1928, in *Bulletin of the Folk-Song Society of the Northeast*, No. 4 (Cambridge, 1932), p. 13. Last phrase of first stanza in broadside is replaced by "Northwest of Amerikay" from Nesbitt's variant text for ease of singing with his tune. Two other broadside variants are at Yale University (Beinecke Library). LAWS D1.

2.

The Poor Armourer Boy. W. in broadside, Loomis and Richards, Middletown (Conn.) in New York Public Library, probably by Richard Alsop of Hartford. Registered by J.R. Jewitt, March 8, 1815. One of two slightly variant broadsides, the other being at one time in the Frank C. Deering Coll., reproduced in the article by Edward S. Meany, Jr. "The Later Life of John R. Jewitt", BCHQ IV-3. Only the second lines of the first stanza differ. In a preamble to the song the broadside claims it to be "Imitated from the Poor Cabin Boy", by Didbin (Charles, Thomas, Thomas the younger?) of which after diligent searching I have found no trace. M. by PJT.

3.

Annexation 1846. W. by "Travelling Bachelor", first published in "Bentley's Miscellany", London, 1846. Repr. John Sheehan, ed., *The Bentley Ballads* (London, 1869), pp. 25-6. This is a reworking of "Yankee Doodle", qv. Sigmund Spaeth, *A History of Popular Music* (New York, 1948), pp. 15-21.

4.

Chief Douglas' Daughter. Although A.S. Farwell notes in his diary, Jan. 10, 1864- Jan. 25, 1867, the song was written by Ben Griffin, who ran Victoria's Boomerang Hotel, it was possibly by Charles T. Seymour, who wrote "The Dredger"; of three mss. in PABC, one is in Seymour's hand. The song is a reworking of Thomas Campbell's "Lord Ullin's Daughter" of c. 1825, qv. *Davidson's Universal Melodist* (London, 1871?), Vol. 1, p. 424, and Edward Bunting, *A General Collection of The Ancient Music of Ireland*, London, 1809 (repr. Dublin: Waltons, 1969, pp. 1-3). M. *Davidson's Universal Melodist*. (The marriages took place August 27, 1861 at Port Townsend, Washington, and August 31, at Victoria.)

5.

The Dredger. W. from ms. in PABC ("The Song of the Dredger"), by Charles T. (?) Seymour dated 1867, New Westminster. M. "Unfortunate Miss Bailey" as sung by PJT, as remembered from the singing of Richard Dyer-Bennett; last line adapted for repetition. (cf. Chappell, *The Ballad Literature and Popular Music of Olden Time*, London, 1858/9, Vol. II, p. 719. The tune was also used for "The Hunters of Kentucky". Stanza 4.1 has been altered from "My namesake can't tell what to do," the namesake being Frederick Seymour, the Governor of the Crown Colony of British Columbia.

6.

Far From Home. W., "W.H.D.". Emory's Bar, Fraser River, July, 1859, in *Hutching's California Magazine* September, 1859, p. 108. M, PJT. I have used stanzas 1, 2, 5, 6, 8, 11 and 12 of the original 12, and have omitted the last chorus. Original w. & m., see "Home Again" in Reddall and Buck, *Songs That Never Die* (U.S.A. n.p., 1894), p. 165.

7.

The Young Man From Canada. W., SAWNEY, pp. 43-5. A reworking of "I'm A Young Man From The Country But You Don't Get Over Me" (London, c. 1862). Stanzas of SAWNEY 3/4 and 9/10 conflated, and slight emendations by PJT appear here in 1.5 (i.e. stanza 1, line 5), 2.8, 4.4, 5.5, 5.7, 6.3, 7.1, 7.3, 7.5-7. Final couplet (8.7-8) is by PJT. Tune is that of original song, indicated in SAWNEY as "Young Man from the Countree." Earlier I put this song to the tune of "Tramps, and Hawkers", qv. my article and song selection "B.C. Songs" in *British Columbia Library Quarterly*, Vol. 26, No. 1 (July 1962), p. 26.

8.

Old Faro. W., SAWNEY, pp. 49-50, with tune indicated as "Peter Gray". In the late 1860's there were two "Peter Gray" songs, differing in form only in their choruses. "Old Faro" was a reworking of the one preserved in Henry de Marsan's *New Comic and Sentimental Singer's Journal*, Vol. I, No. 15, p. 84 (c. 1868), the tune of which has not yet been found. W. & m., chorus, slightly adapted to fit the surviving tune as sung by PJT. Stanzas 3 and 6 omitted.

9.

Bonnie Are The Hurdies O! W., SAWNEY, pp. 15-6; previously appeared in *Cariboo Sentinel* of July 23, 1866. A reworking of "Green Grow the Rashes, O", itself a reworking by Burns (1784) of an earlier "Rustic song", first printed 1549. M. after James C. Dick, *The Songs of Robert Burns* (repr. Hatboro, 1962), p. 102.

10.

Mary, Come Home. W. by "Mosquito", first appeared in *Cariboo Sentinel* of February 13, 1869. M., "Come Home, Father", c Henry C. Work, 1864.

11.

The Skedaddler. W. in ms. by J. Lawrence in *Horsefly*, 1865 in PABC. M., PJT, after "Rye Whiskey".

12.

Song of the "Dominion Boys" in British Columbia. W., anon., appeared in *Cariboo Sentinel* of June 19, 1869. A reworking of "Tramp, Tramp, Tramp", w. and m. by G.F. Root, 1864.

13.

Cheer, Boys, Cheer for the Dominion Nation. W., SAWNEY pp. 56-7; an edited version of the original, which appeared in *Cariboo Sentinel* of December 5, 1868. A reworking of "Cheer, Boys, Cheer", w. and m. by C. Booth, c. 1850.

14.

Seattle Illahee. From the singing of Capt. W.R. Hall, Campbell River, 1959 and 1962. PJT Coll. #370. Other fragments of variants collected from Herbert Clark, Keremeos, 1970 ("Come, Klootchman", PJT. Coll. #132), Louis Thompson, Vaseux Lake, 1961 ("Hiyu Clams and Mowitch", PJT. Coll. #145), and Nels McKim, Pritchard, 1964 ("Seattle Illahee", PJT Coll. #466). Ms. of another version, quoted in notes, are in B.A. McKelvie papers, PABC.

15.

My Name, 'Tis Vernon Fetterly. From the singing of Vernon Fetterly, Okanagan Falls, 1961. PJT Coll. #121. Text collated by PJT. The song is a variant of "The Arkansas Traveller", qv. LAWS H1.

16.

The Old Go-Hungry Hashhouse. W., m., as sung by PJT, learned from Ed Dalby, Campbell River, 1959, with additional words by PJT (v. 2 and 3.4-6). Cf. Douglas Gilbert, *Lost Chords* (New York, 1942), pp. 191-2.

17.

Klondike! From the singing of Capt. Charles Cates, Vancouver, 1959. PJT Coll. #159. W. and m. are as Capt. Cates learned them from his father; but note the slight but significant variation of tune in Edith Fowke et al., *Canada's Story in Song* (Toronto, 1960) p. 186. Cf. for original in W.T. Stead, ed., *The Review of Reviews*, Vol XVI, July-December 1897, London, pp. 243-4. It seems that it first appeared in the *Daily Chronicle* as comic Cockney dialect verse by "Tompkins".

18.

Hip-Hip-Hoorah. From the singing of Vern Seidelman, Vancouver, 1973, who learned it as a child at Mud Bay School, northwest of Boundary Bay, PJT Coll. #300. Stanza 1:G read orig. "Sugar Maples".

19.

The Pembina River Homestead. From the singing of J.C. "Jim" Akers, Lillooet, 1973. PJT Coll. #399. W., m., singer.

20.

Where The Great Peace River Flows. W., my six stanza collation from ten texts ranging in length from one to seven stanzas, nine of the texts collected by Cecil Pickell of Fort St. John in response to a request by him in the *Alaska Highway News* of August 23, 1972 for words to the song. A seven stanza selection from the responses was printed in the *Alaska Highway News* of September 6, 1972. M., from the singing of Cecil P. Pickell, Fort St. John, 1965. PJT Coll. #498. Where the complete tune of "Where the Shannon River Flows" is used, two informants indicated the chorus was stanza 5, and another used stanza 4.

21.

The Banks Of The Similkameen. From the singing of Jim Kehoe, Anarchist Mountain, nr. Osoyoos, 1963. PJT Coll. #098. Other variants collected from Herbert Clark, Keremeos, 1970 (PJT Coll. #131) and from Bruce Chapman, Okanagan Falls, 1970 (PJT Coll. #140). A variant of "The Lake of Ponchartrain", qv. LAWS H9.

22.

Moosehunter's Blues. From the singing of Bobby Ball, Telegraph Creek, 1974. PJT Coll. #493. W., m., singer.

23.

Drill, Ye Tarriers, Drill. W. selected from a text in the *Vancouver Sun* of May 16, 1931, p. 4. The stanzas came from readers who a week previously had been requested to "supply as many stanzas as possible for publication." The printed texts of fourteen and one-half stanzas included not only those which sprang from the original as credited to Thomas F. Casey, an Irish American, published in 1888, but also many added apparently by railroad construction workers in western Canada. The chorus was printed with two variations: ". . . workin' on the Shuswap Railway" and ". . . workin' on the Canadian Pacific Railway". I have shortened it to "...working on the C.P. Railway". The author of the *Sun* article, Doris S. Milligan, informed me that this was the only old song the paper

published at that time. M., traditional as sung by PJT. Cf. the singing of Nels McKim, Pritchard, 1964, PJT Coll. #457 and "Drill Ye Heroes Drill" in Kenneth Peacock's *Songs of the Newfoundland Outports* (Ottawa, 1965), Vol III, pp. 781-2.

24.

Teaming Up The Cariboo Road. A reworking of a Tin Pan Alley minstrel song, "Climbing up the Golden Stairs", © 1884. Chorus as sung by Gerald Currie, Chase, 1964: PJT Coll. #413. Stanzas 1 and 2, a collation of two fragments, one from G. Currie, the other collected by Bert Hughes in 1948 and printed with news story (*Vancouver Sun* of September 22, 1948) with the last four lines of stanza 2 taken from the original minstrel song. Stanzas 1.3-6 and 3 by PJT. The song refers to Gerald Currie's grandfather. M., from Gerald Currie and original tune. Cf. Ira W. Ford, *Traditional Music in America* (New York, 1940), p. 38.

25.

Where The Fraser River Flows. W., by Joe Hill, organizer for the Industrial Workers of the World, first printed in the *Industrial Worker* (Spokane, Wash.), May 9, 1912. The text printed here is faithful to Hill's except for the last line of the chorus, which read in the original: "And we're going to win the day, boys, where the River Fraser flows." "River Fraser" is both unidiomatic and a tongue-twister when sung with drive, the usual way the song has been treated in recent years in British Columbia. Today the last line of stanza 1 is usually sung: "To *rally* round *the* standard when the Red Flag is unfurled." The song reportedly appeared in the 4th edition (1912) of the IWW songster, called on the title page *Songs of the Workers* and on the cover *IWW Songs to Fan the Flames of Discontent.* I have seen Hill's text in both the 9th edition (1916) and the 15th edition (1919), but the song was deleted by the 17th edition (1921). On its reappearance in the songster in the 29th edition (published in 1956 for the 50th anniversary of the IWW), a few words had regrettably been altered. In the first stanza, perhaps to simplify the grammar, "clear contention" replaced Hill's "fixed intention", and "That we should all" replaced "And I hope you'll all". I mention these details to clear up some confusion which has arisen, since the IWW songsters are still available; the latest edition is the 34th (1973). I hope the 35th edition will return to the Joe Hill text or at least acknowledge it. That Hill's song had some currency in British Columbia is testified to by some of his words being retained in a song using the Lardeau River. See also P.J. Thomas, "Where the rivers flow", *Canadian Folk Music Journal*, Vol. 3 (1975), pp. 47-55 and corrigendum. M., an adaptation of the tune in B. Stavis and F. Harmon, *Songs of Joe Hill* (New York: People's Artists, Inc., 1955), itself rooted in "Where the River Shannon Flows", the tune indicated by Hill.

26.

The P.G.E. Song. From the singing of Keith Crowe, Vancouver, 1959. W., m., singer, written at Summit Lake, 1949. When singing the song, Keith Crowe sometimes changed the names mentioned. Cf. *Singalong*, Vol. 2, No. 1 (July, 1958).

27.

The Minto. From the singing of K.M. "Mutt" Papov, Nakusp, 1973, who learned it about 1954 from an anonymous submission to the *Arrow Lakes News* of Nakusp. M., singer and friend. PJT Coll. #061.

28.

Fort Nelson Freighter's Song. Ms. from Cecil Pickell, Fort St. John, c. 1965; to be sung to "The Wabash Cannonball".

29.

The Wreck of the C.P. Yorke. From the singing of Stanley G. Triggs, Vancouver, 1961. PJT Coll. #235. W., m., singer. Cf. Stanley G. Triggs, *Bunkhouse and Forecastle Songs of the Northwest*, Folkways FG 3569.

30.

Truck Driver's Song. From the singing of M.K. "Mutt" Papov, Nakusp, 1973. PJT Coll. #062. W., m., singer.

31.

Way Up The Ucletaw. Words from the singing of Ed Dalby, Campbell River, 1959, stanza 1 by PJT. M., PJT from Dalby.

32.

Buck's Camp Down At Monroe. W., from the singing of Ed Dalby, Campbell River, 1959. M., PJT from Dalby, who first heard it on Vancouver Island, c. 1900.

33.

The Potlatch Fair. From the singing of Capt. W.R. "Bill" Hall; Campbell River, 1959. PJT Coll. #369. Appears to be a reworking of "Ole From North Dakota", the latter seen in a detached clipping, possibly from *Family Herald and Weekly Star*, Montreal, now in author's library.

34.

The Grand Hotel. From the singing of Bennett King Lesley, Vancouver, 1975. PJT Coll. #306. Cf. another variant collected in Vancouver in the early 'fifties by Ed McCurdy and published in Edith Fowke, *Folk Songs of Canada* (Waterloo, 1954), p. 180.

35.

The Greenchain Song. From the singing of Don Fraser, Vancouver, 1973, and learned from its author, J.F. "Jim" Monroe, a forester for many years in northern B.C. and the Kootenays, now of Ottawa. PJT Coll. #249.

36.

Way Up On The Monashee Range. W., George Winkler, "Itchy Feet" in *Songs of the Okanagan* (Vernon, 1946), p. 16, rearranged by PJT with permission of author. M., PJT. George Winkler, who was known as "the prospector-poet", died in 1978, aged 104.

37.

Are You From Bevan? Chorus from the singing of John Strachan, Union Bay, 1969: PJT Coll. #353. See also a variant collected from James "Shaky" Robertson, Columbus, Ohio in George Korson, *Coal Dust on the Fiddle* (Philadelphia, 1943) p. 425. Verses by PJT. The song is a reworking of "Are You From Dixie?" c. 1915. Cf. "Are You A Wobbly?" in *I.W.W. Songs to Fan the Flames of Discontent* (Chicago, 1973: 34th ed.) p. 49. First appearance in songbook, 21st ed., 1925.

38.

Bowser's Seventy Twa. From the singing of Dick Morgan, Ladysmith, 1962: PJT Coll. #351. Fragments collected from George Gold, Ladysmith, 1962: PJT Coll. #371. It was first printed in the *B.C. Federationist*, November 7, 1913 (without a chorus) and April 24, 1914 (with a chorus). The accompanying note read: "The Nanaimo Miners' Committee sends the *Federationist* a copy of a song favourite with the miners. It was composed by R.W. Smith and was sung with success by Wm. J. Willis." Printed in Edith Fowke, "Labour and Industrial Protest Songs in Canada", *Journal of American Folklore*, Vol. 82, No. 323 (January-March 1969), p. 37.

39.

Hard Rock Miner. From the singing of Joe Irving Sr., Castlegar, 1970. PJT Coll. #054. Also collected from Hazel Irving, Castlegar, 1970 (PJT Coll. #048), Luigi del Puppo, Nelson, 1970 (PJT Coll. #072), Keith O'Brien, Vancouver, c. 1965 (PJT Coll. #313), and Barry Black, Alberni, 1964 (PJT Coll. #374). Ms. from Del Black, c. 1962. The song is a reworking of "When You Wore a Tulip", c. 1914. Cf. LINGENFELTER, p. 145.

40.

Taku Miners. From the singing of Bill and Audrey Lore, Tahsis, 1972. Bill Lore: "As far as I know, that was written, most of it, by a man in jail in Juneau from the Taku mine." M., "Clementine" and "The Irish Washerwoman". PJT Coll. #343.

41.

I'm Only A Broken Down Mucker. From the singing of Bill Booth, Coquitlam, 1973. PJT Coll. #314. Ms. in possession of Hugh and Florida Town, who sang with Bill Booth in the Lost Dog Singers, a folk song group, in Kimberley, 1960—c. 1967. Cf. a fragment collected by Michael J. Weiss in 1971 at Wells, in *Canadian Folk Music Journal*, Vol. 1 (1973). M., "I've Got No Use For the Women", qv. LINGENFELTER, p. 434.

42.

The Doryman. From Ralph W. Andrews and A.K. Larsen, *Fish and Ships* (Seattle, 1959), p. 71. A.K. Larsen: "I found a typewritten copy of 'The Doryman' in a locker I was cleaning out on joining the diesel schooner *Aleutian* in 1939. I showed it to the rest of the crew but they knew nothing of its origin." (Interview by PJT, May 30, 1974). M., PJT.

43.

The Song Of The Sockeye. W., Ross Cumbers, c. 1940. M., PJT. The verses were found c. 1960 by Nick Guthrie, now of Courtenay, under a glass-covered notice-board at the deserted Wadhams Cannery on Rivers Inlet.

44.

The Pender Harbour Fisherman. From the singing of Gordon Klein, North Vancouver, 1953. PJT Coll. #250. A reworking of "The Great American Bum" by Harry "Haywire Mac" McClintock. Qv. LINGENFELTER p. 532.

45.

Bring Back That Gillnet To Me. From the singing of Leo Harris, Port Coquitlam, 1974. PJT Coll. #304. W., singer (c. 1939) to tune of "My Bonnie Lies Over the Ocean".

46.

The Young British Rancher. W., *Honest Injun*, Vol. I, No. 2, p. 12 (Victoria, November 6, 1897). The copy in Special Collections at UBC bears an indication in pencil of the author ("J. Cartmel"). A reworking of Kipling's "Young British Soldier", qv. *Barrack Room Ballads* London, 1892. M., PJT.

47.

Sunset. Ms. (and tune indicated) from Mrs. K. Lacey, Osoyoos, 1963. Tune "Once in the Saddle", i.e. "The Cowboy's Lament", here as sung by Stanley Botting, Naramata, 1961: PJT Coll. #113.

48.

Tying A Knot In The Devil's Tail. From the singing of Ronnie Craig, Deadman's Creek, 1973: PJT Coll. #412. Also collected from Stanley Botting, Naramata, 1961: PJT Coll. #115: Nels McKim, Pritchard, 1964: PJT Coll. #458. Cf. LAWS B17: LINGENFELTER p. 358 and Fife and Fife, *Cowboy and Western Songs* (New York, 1969) pp. 201-3.

49.

Hangin' In The Barn. From the singing of John Kehoe, Osoyoos, 1970, who told me he learned it from its author, Percy Gould, "an old-time cowboy, used to ride in Calgary." PJT Coll. #106.

Bibliography

The following references were useful in the preparation of this work. Printed and manuscript sources of songs are given in the Appendix.

Private Papers

Arthur S. Farwell. Diary: Jan. 10, 1864-Jan. 25, 1867. Provincial Archives of British Columbia.

Public Documents and Records

British Columbia. Attorney-General, Miscellaneous Official Correspondence. Provincial Archives of British Columbia.

British Columbia Legislative Council debate on the subject of confederation with Canada. Victoria: Government Printer, 1870. (Reprinted 1912.)

Colonial Government Correspondence. PABC.

Colonial Office Records and Correspondence. PABC.

Colonial Secretary, Miscellaneous Official Correspondence. PABC.

Dugas, C.A., F. Pedley, and J. Appleton. "Report of the commissioners in re Crow's Nest complaints." *Sessional papers, House of Commons,* Vol. XXXII, No. 13, Miscellaneous, 61 Victoria, No. 90A. 1898.

Price, Samuel. *The report of royal commissioner on coal mining disputes on Vancouver Island.* Ottawa: Gov't. Printing Bureau, 1913.

Newspapers

New Westminster *British Columbian*
Spokane *Industrial Worker*
Vancouver *Daily Province*
Vancouver *Sun*
Victoria *Daily Colonist*
Victoria *Times*

General Printed Sources: Books, Articles and Pamphlets

Bancroft, Hubert H. *History of British Columbia: 1792-1887.* 1887. (Reprinted New York: Arno Press, 1967.)

Bergren, Myrtle. *Tough timber: the loggers of British Columbia — their story.* Toronto: Progress Books, 1966.

Bowes, Gordon E. (ed.) *Peace River chronicles.* Vancouver: Prescott, 1963.

Bryant, Ralph Clement. *Logging: the principles and general methods.* 2nd ed. New York: John Wiley and sons, 1923.

Cotsworth, Moses B. *Railway bungling, and worse, in British Columbia,* Vancouver: C. Appleby, [1918].

Dawson, C.A. *The settlement of the Peace River country: a study of a pioneer area.* Toronto: Macmillan, 1934.

Duff, Wilson and Michael Kew. "Anthony Island, a home of the Haidas" in *British Columbia Provincial Museum Annual report for 1957.*

Emmons, G.T. *The Tahltan Indians.* Philadelphia: The University Museum, 1911.

Friesen, J. and H.K. Ralston. *Historical Essays on British Columbia.* Toronto: McClelland and Stewart, 1976.

Gosnell, R.E. *A history of British Columbia.* Victoria: Lewis Pub. Co. 1906.

Gosnell, R.E. *A history of British Columbia Part II.* Victoria and Vancouver: B.C. Historical Society, 1913. (Bound with E.O.S. Scholefield's *Part I* under the combined title *British Columbia: sixty years of progress.*)

Hedley, Rev. John N. *The Labour trouble in Nanaimo district.* Nanaimo, B.C.: 1913 (pamphlet).

Howay, F.W. *The early history of the Fraser River mines (Archives of British Columbia memoir no. VI).* Victoria: King's Printer, 1926.

Howay, F.W. *Voyages of the "Columbia" to the northwest coast, 1787-1790 and 1790-1793.* Boston: Massachusetts Historical Society, 1941.

Innis, Harold A. *A history of the Canadian Pacific Railway.* 1923. (Reprinted Toronto: University of Toronto Press, 1970)

Jamieson, Stuart M. *Study no. 22, Task Force on Labour Relations. Times of trouble: labour unrest and industrial conflict in Canada, 1900-1966.* Ottawa: Information Canada, 1968.

Jenness, Diamond. *Indians of Canada.* Ottawa: National Museum of Canada, 1932.

Jensen, Vernon H. *Lumber and labour.* New York: Farrar and Rinehart, 1945.

Jewitt, John R. *A journal kept at Nootka Sound: one of the surviving crew of the ship "Boston"....* Boston: 1807. (Reprinted Boston: Goodspeed, 1931.)

Knox, Paul and Philip Resnick (eds.) *Essays in B.C. political economy.* Vancouver: New Star, 1974.

Lamb, W. Kaye. *History of the Canadian Pacific Railway.* New York: Macmillan, 1975.

Lavallee, Omer. *Van Horne's road.* Montreal: Railfare enterprises, 1974.

Lawrence, Guy. *40 years on the Yukon telegraph.* Vancouver: Mitchell Press, 1965.

Lipton, Charles. *The trade union movement in Canada 1827-1959.* 3rd ed. Toronto: N.C. Press, 1973.

Logan, Harold, A. *The history of trade union organization in Canada.* Chicago: University of Chicago Press, 1928.

Logan, Harold A. *Trade unions in Canada: their development and functioning.* Toronto: Macmillan, 1948.

Lyons, Cecily. *Salmon — our heritage.* Vancouver: Mitchell Press, 1969.

McCormick, A. Ross *Reformers, rebels, and revolutionaries: the western Canadian radical movement 1899-1919.* Toronto: U. of T. Press, 1977

McCulloch, Walter F. *Woods words: a comprehensive dictionary of loggers' terms.* Oregon Hist. Society and Champoeg Press, 1958.

Money, Anton. "Voyage up the Stikine." *Alaska Sportsman,* Vol. XXX, Nos. 8 and 9, Aug. and Sept., 1964.

Morice, A.G. *History of the northern interior of British Columbia.* Toronto: Briggs, 1904.

Myers, Gustavus. *History of Canadian wealth.* Chicago: Kerr, 1914. (Reprinted Toronto: James Lewis and Samuel, 1972.)

Ormsby, Margaret. *British Columbia: a history.* Toronto: Macmillan, 1958, reprinted with corrections, 1971.

Peele, Robert. *Mining engineer's handbook,* Vol. I and II, 2nd. ed. New York: John Wiley and Son, 1927.

Phillips, Paul A. *No power greater: a century of labour in British Columbia.* Vancouver: B.C. Federation of Labour and Boag Foundation, 1967.

Ramsay, Bruce. *P.G.E.: railway to the north.* Vancouver: Mitchell Press, 1962.

Regher, T.D. "William Mackenzie, Donald Mann and the larger Canada." in A.W. Raporich (ed.) *Western Canada: Past and Present.* Calgary: University of Calgary and McClelland and Stewart, 1975.

Robin, Martin. *Radical politics and Canadian labour 1880-1930.* Kingston: Industrial Relations Centre, Queen's University, 1968.

Robin, Martin. *The rush for spoils: the company province 1871-1933.* Toronto: McClelland and Stewart, 1972.

Scott, Jack. *Plunderbund and proletariat: a history of the I.W.W. in B.C.* Vancouver: New Star, 1975.

Shelton, W.G. ed. *British Columbia and confederation.* Victoria: University of Victoria, 1967.

Smith, Dorothy Blakey. *James Douglas: father of British Columbia.* Toronto: Oxford University Press, 1971.

Smith, Gibbs. M. *Joe Hill.* Salt Lake City: University of Utah Press, 1969.

Smith, Marion B. "The Lady Nobody Knows" in R. Watters (ed.) *British Columbia—a centennial anthology.* Toronto: McClelland and Stewart, 1958.

Thompson, William F. and Norman L. Freeman. *Report of the International Fisheries Commission no. 5: history of the Pacific halibut fishery.* Vancouver: Wrigley Printing Co., 1930.

Underwood, Marsh. *The log of a logger.* Portland: Kilham, 1938.

Van Kirk, Sylvia. "The custom of the country." *Essays in western history in honour of Lewis Gwynne Thomas.* ed. by Lewis H. Thomas. Edmonton: University of Alberta Press, 1976.

Ventress, C., M. Davies and E. Kyllo. *The peacemakers of North Peace.* Fort St. John: Davies, Ventress and Kyllo, 1973.

Waite, P.B. *The life and times of confederation 1864-1867.* Toronto: University of Toronto Press, 1962.

Walbran, Capt. John T. *British Columbia coastal names 1592-1906 their origin and history.* 1909 Govt. Printing Bureau, Ottawa.

Wilson, Charles. *Mapping the frontier: Charles Wilson's diary of the survey of the 49th parallel 1858-1862... Edited... by George F.G. Stanley.* Toronto: Macmillan, 1970.

Index of Titles and First Lines

Index

Place names are in British Columbia unless otherwise indicated.
The Page numbers in italics refer to maps and/or illustrations.

PRINTED IN CANADA